Copper plate from Etowah mound, Georgia.

INDIAN LEGENDS OF THE AMERICAN

Indian
Legends

LYONS AND CARNAHAN

CHICAGO WILKES-BARRE DALLAS ATLANTA PASADENA PORTLAND

OF
EASTERN
AMERICA

by JOHANNA R. M. LYBACK

COLOR ILLUSTRATIONS AND MAP ORNAMENTATION BY DICK WEST

OTHER ILLUSTRATIONS BY ALEXANDER KEY

About the Artist. Walter Richard West is one of the leading Indian artists of our time. His award-winning works have been exhibited in the Smithsonian Institution, and he has had important showings in galleries both here and abroad. Mr. West's talents for wood carving and ceramics have also brought him a number of awards.

Mr. West was educated at the Concho Indian School, Haskell Institute, Bacone College, University of Redlands, and University of Oklahoma (where he earned the degrees of B.F.A. and M.F.A.). In May, 1962, Mr. West accepted the honorary degree of Doctor of Humane Letters from Eastern Baptist College in Philadelphia. He now serves as Director of the Art Department of Bacone College.

The paintings herein, which were commissioned by Lyons and Carnahan expressly for this book, have been displayed at several Indian expositions. They are now on permanent exhibit at Gilcrease Institute of Fine Arts in Tulsa, Oklahoma.

INTRODUCTION

Until the coming of the Europeans, this country was inhabited solely by a race now known, for want of a better name, as the American Indian. This people was composed of various families or tribes, alike in general appearance, but speaking different tongues and usually at war with one another. They lived largely by hunting and fishing. While they did not have marked boundaries, each clan generally occupied a certain definite territory, until driven out by some stronger confederation.

The men were tall and erect, with skin of bronze or brown hue. Their cheek bones were high, eyes piercing and dark, and, like most primitive people, their foreheads were inclined to slope backward. Their hair was coarse, straight, and black. Some of them shaved their heads, leaving only a scalp lock near the center. This was ornamented with the feather of an eagle, hawk, crow or other wild bird that suited the fancy of the wearer. All, or nearly all, kept their faces free of the thin Indian beard. They wore little clothing, and this after the fashion of leggings, frocks, blankets, and tunics easily made. These garments were made from the skins of animals or feathers of birds.

The young women were slender, comely, and vivacious, but like all primitive races, they lost the grace and freshness and beauty of youth at an early age. They married young and performed their daily rounds of drudgery without complaint. They made their warrior-husbands' moccasins with an honest pride in their skill. They lived their simple lives without dreams of a wider field of usefulness. As old women they became the historians of their tribes. Trained to do this, one of them could sit at some council and years later repeat every word that was said, and describe every act, with remarkable fidelity to truth.

The children romped in the sun or played at hunting the deer in the shadow of the forest, and whiled away the days without a thought for the future. Men found delight in the chase, which may have wound through the trackless forest for a hundred miles. They found the height of pleasure in the wildwood festival, which might last for days. They sated their appetites at the feast and were contented. They endured days of fasting without a murmur. So, in the charity of their simple faith, according to their light, theirs was not an unhappy lot.

It would be futile to try to trace the origin of the aborigines of America. Any argument that might be advanced could be disputed. Not one pre-Columbian relic, implement, inscription, object of art or architecture has been found on this continent indicating an Old World origin.

Of all primitive peoples the North American Indians were the ideal children of Nature; and had their mythology been preserved before the white man's misunderstanding had destroyed its wild metaphors and picturesque similes, American literature would have been enriched by a mythology grander than that of the Aryans, purer than that of the Greeks, richer in its wealth of imagination than that of the Northmen. Without a written language themselves, except that of symbols, rude signs, and hieroglyphics, only fragments remain to us of that wonderful dream of untutored life. Whoever has preserved for us any part of this wildwood drama has done a lasting favor. If only there could have been more with an understanding and appreciation of the Indian's good qualities! Had there been more Apostle Eliots and William Penns, his fate might have been cast in more hopeful lines!

The American aborigine was a natural story-teller. Seeing, as he did, an omen in every shifting shade of the clouds, a sign in the changing leaf, a token of beauty or ugliness in the different places of the wildwood, he knew no rock nor river, lake nor mountain, valley nor hillside that did not speak of some attraction, some vision of race, some deed of valor, some incident of love or remembrance of wrong. These memories lived in stories that were told and retold to each succeeding generation, from time immemorial. They were told with lowered voice and air of mystery, each myth fraught with the fantasy of Nature's solitude, and each legend bordered with the fringe of the silver foam of superstition. "Speak softly," warned the dusky boatman to the Jesuit Father Albanel, as he plied the paddles of his canoe under the frowning ramparts of the mountain overhanging Lake Mistassini, "or the Spirit of the Cliff will be angry with us, and send his storm gods to out-ride our canoe and drown us all."

The Indian, like a child, had a mind remarkably acute in one direction, but undeveloped in others. He could grasp but one truth, and that without any great abstract reasoning. He could not build a house. He could not even wield an ax with any skill. Still he could shape his stone implements with wonderful patience and cunning. Even if a movement did not stir a stick, his swift vision never failed to detect the least commotion in the solitude. These were qualities his pale-browed rival could not imitate.

A shadow himself, the child of the forest believed all alike passed to Spirit Land, where they continued the pursuits begun here. It was in truth a Land of Shades, where trees, flowers, animals, men—all things were spirits.

"By midnight moons, o'er moistening dews,
    In vestments for the chase arrayed,
The hunter still the deer pursues,
    The hunter and the deer a shade."

G. WALDO BROWNE.

Contents

THE New England STATES

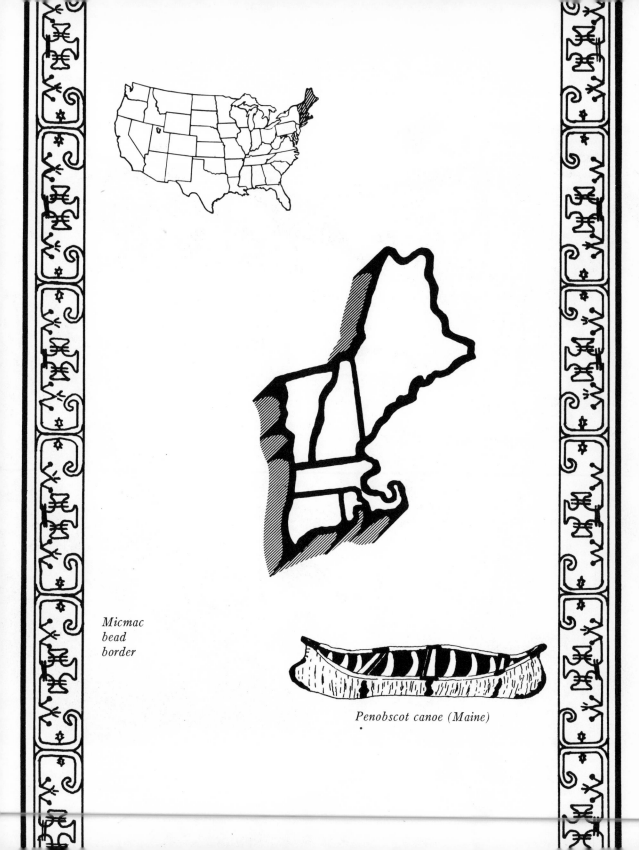

Micmac
bead
border

Penobscot canoe (Maine)

Dick West

Legends of Maine

GLOOSKAP

Long, long ago the animals could talk, and they were wiser than men. Then the god Glooskap began to teach men. He taught them to make wigwams, instead of seeking shelter in caves. He taught them which roots and herbs could be used as food or medicine. He taught them what animals were good for food, and showed them how to prepare the meat. He filled the waters with fish, and showed men how to catch them.

Glooskap was the greatest of the gods. He often had to settle quarrels between the other gods. They accepted his judgment.

When Glooskap wished to do good he took the shape of a giant. When he wished to punish the wicked he made himself still larger. He made himself so tall that his head touched the stars.

Glooskap was the friend of both men and animals. He talked with the animals, and they understood him. When the palefaces came Glooskap bade his friends, both men and animals, farewell, and disappeared. No one ever saw him again.

THE TALE OF MOOSEHEAD LAKE

Glooskap was very fond of hunting. When he went on a long hunting trip he always carried a large kettle in which to cook his food.

Once he followed a moose cow and calf a long way, but they ran so fast he could not catch up with them. Glooskap began to feel tired. The kettle seemed to get heavier and heavier. At last he threw it away. As it fell to the ground it turned to stone. It was called Kettle Mountain ever after.

Now Glooskap could run faster, and he caught up with the moose and killed them. Then he turned them to stone. To this day the cow lies by the lake where she fell, and it is called Moosehead Lake.

✳   ✳   ✳

Moosehad Lake is the largest lake in New England. It spreads out in the shape of two gigantic horns, and Mount Kineo, on the shore, is supposed to be the head of the moose. It consists of hornstone, which the Indians used for arrowheads. This is the largest body of this stone that has yet been found in the world.

THE LEGEND OF SACO RIVER

Long, long ago there were goblins around Mount Katahdin. They roamed the country, killing and eating red men, and stealing from them.

When Glooskap heard of this he came to help the red men. He changed himself into a goblin, and changed half of his body to stone. At first the goblins thought he was a beggar, and they treated him very badly. Then they began to think he was a wizard. They wanted to show him that they were smarter than he, and tried many tricks with him.

When Glooskap decided they had carried on long enough, he stamped his foot on the ground. Then all the streams that were hidden in the mountains burst forth. Saco came rushing with such a roar that it sounded as if the whole world were breaking up. He swept the goblins with him and carried them out to the great sea. Then Glooskap changed them into fish.

$$\ast \quad \ast \quad \ast$$

The course of the Saco is an almost constant chain of rushing, roaring falls.

THE BRIDE OF KATAHDIN

Long, long ago some maidens of the Penobscot tribe went to pick berries on the slopes of Katahdin. They looked up at the mountain and spoke of how grand and beautiful it was. One of them said, "When I get a husband I hope he will be like Katahdin."

The others laughed at her. Then she felt

ashamed, and went up higher, where they could not see her. When they were ready to return they called her, but she did not come. They went home thinking she would soon follow them. But she did not return for three years.

Then one day she came, leading a little boy by the hand. He was different from other children. His cheeks and brows were of stone. When he pointed at a bird or an animal it fell down, dead. So now the tribe was never without food.

But one day some of them spoke insulting words to his mother. Then she became angry. She told them her child was the son of the spirit of Katahdin. His father had intended that he should found a mighty race, which would rule the earth. She said they should have seen who he was. Had they not seen that he was different from other children? Had they not seen his cheeks and brows of stone? Had they not seen his wonderful power over birds and animals? After this he would no longer use it for them. They could hunt their own game.

When she had said this she took her boy by the hand and went toward the mountain. She never returned. The Penobscots had been a large and powerful tribe. After this they began to dwindle and grow poor.

✶ ✶ ✶

The Penobscot tribe was once the richest and most powerful in that part of the country. They gave their name to the river which flowed through their land, and to their capital, which was near Bangor. The remainder of the tribe now live on an island in this river, near Oldtown. They do not live in wigwams, but have built houses, and they have a church, a school and a town hall.

THE HUNT ON MOUNT DESERT ISLAND

Glooskap once took his bow and arrows and went hunting on Mount Desert Island. He killed a large moose. He threw part of it at the place we call Bar Harbor, and the rest he threw across the water. Both parts turned to stone, and lie there to this day.

✶   ✶   ✶

Mount Desert is the largest island on the coast of Maine. It was discovered by two early French explorers, Sieur De Monts and Samuel Champlain. When they saw the mountain peaks far out at sea they named it Mount Desert Island.

It is now the Lafayette National Park. The numerous sea fowl along the coast find a refuge and a resting place there.

THE SPIRIT OF KATAHDIN

Long, long ago a man once went hunting around Mount Katahdin. He was there many weeks, but did not see another human being. Then one day he saw tracks of a pair of snowshoes. The next day he saw them again, but they were in another place. He saw them the next day, and the next, for many days. But they were always in a different place.

One day he followed the tracks. He came to a place where there were many other tracks. There were so many they had made a path. The hunter followed the path. It led toward the mountain, and ended at the base of a precipice. While he stood there wondering he heard footsteps. Then a tall, fine looking maiden came to him. The hunter was afraid at first, but she asked him, very kindly, to follow her.

They went up against the mountain wall. The maiden touched it, and it turned to mist. They went through it, and went farther and farther into the mountain.

In the very heart of the mountain there was a cave. There sat the spirit of Katahdin. He welcomed them kindly, and asked the maiden if her brothers had come. She answered that she heard them coming. The hunter saw a flash and heard a sound, as of thunder. Then two giants entered the cave. They were very handsome, but their brows and cheeks were of stone. The maiden told the hunter they were her brothers, Thunder and Lightning. Their duty was to protect the friends of

the spirit of Katahdin, and to punish those who did evil.

Very soon their father told them of some wicked deed that was being done, and sent them to punish it.

The giants asked the hunter if he wished to go with them. When he said he did, they adopted him as their brother. Then they showed him how to roam about the sky and send thunder down to the earth. He kept on doing this all day.

When evening came he began to feel afraid again, and wished he was safe at home once more. When the giants saw this they promised to let him go home. They sent a storm over his village, and told him to travel with it. When it was just above his home he fell down as a roaring thunder.

The people who saw him forgot about the storm, and seemed to think of nothing but the hunter. Yet they did not know he had come down as a thunder. All the people in the village came to see him, and they greeted him as if he had never been expected to return.

"Why are you all so surprised to see me?" asked the hunter. "Have I not often stayed away hunting two or three moons?"

"Yes, two or three moons," they answered, "but this time you have been away seven years."

THE GOBLIN

Long, long ago two brothers once went hunting along the Penobscot. They built a lodge in the forest, and stayed a long time. One day, when they were going home with the game, one of them said, "We can not stay much longer, for our clothes and moccasins are wearing out."

His brother answered, "I wish we had a woman to help us. She would mend our clothes, and they would last a while yet."

Just then they saw a deer, and the older brother said, "You may go home with the game. I shall follow the deer."

When the younger brother came to their lodge he saw smoke rising from it. When he went in he saw that it had been cleaned and put in order. The clothes they had left there had been mended. There was a kettle hanging over the fire, with something cooking in it. But the hunter saw no one. He went out and hid in the woods. After a while he saw a beautiful maiden go into the lodge. When he came in she was very shy.

But the hunter treated her with great respect. She stayed, and took care of the lodge. In the evenings, when the hunter returned, they played like children. One evening she said, "Your brother is coming. I am afraid of him."

Then she bade him farewell and went away. But when the older brother heard about the maiden he said, "She need not have been afraid of me. I wish I could have seen her."

Soon after this she came back. She was drawing a sled. It was filled with clothes and weapons. Now the hunters knew they could stay all winter. They found more game than ever before. When spring came they put all the skins in their canoe and started for home. They took the maiden with them. But after a while she said, "Your father would not like me. Set me ashore. Do not tell your father about me."

But the older brother told his father. The father said, "She was no human maiden. It must have been a goblin. It is well she did not come with you."

Then the son feared she might do him or his

brother harm. He rowed up the river to look for her. Soon he saw her. She was bathing in the river. He shot an arrow at her. Then some feathers whirled about over the water, and he saw a partridge fly up. But he did not see the maiden again.

The younger brother often thought of the maiden, and how kind she had been. One day he rowed up the river to look for her. He found her near the lodge. He stayed there several days, and they played as they had done before. When he went away the maiden said, "Your father will choose a wife for you. Do not marry her. If you do all will come to an end."

Soon after the father told him he had chosen him a wife. The son knew he must obey his father. He also knew he could not marry the goblin. So he said, "That is well."

Then they prepared a great wedding feast.

They danced four days. Then they feasted four days longer. At the end of the last day the bridegroom said, "Now comes the end."

Then he lay down on a bear skin and sighed

heavily several times. With the last sigh his spirit went up to the Ghost's Walk (The Milky Way).

Now the father knew that the goblin had taken her revenge. He went away, no one knew whither. After that his tribe became scattered.

THE CHAIR WITH THE WOVEN SEAT

Long, long ago some red men once stood by the sea, watching a strange canoe that was coming toward them. It was larger than any canoe they had seen, and it had wings. It stopped some distance from the shore, and a smaller canoe was lowered from it.

A man with a pale face got into the small canoe and rowed up to them. He had a strange object in the boat. It was a chair. The paleface showed the red men how this could be used. Then he asked if he might have as much of their land as he could set the chair upon, and they let him have it.

The seat of the chair was made of braided cord. The paleface loosened one end of the cord and began to pull it out. He asked the red men if he might go far enough into their land to pull out all of the cord. They let him do so. The paleface went toward the west, he went toward the south, he went toward the north, and before the cord was pulled out he had gone all over the red men's land.

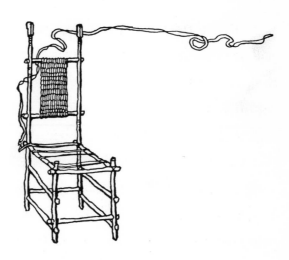

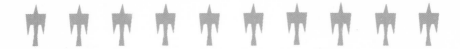

Legends of Massachusetts

THE GIANT MAUSHOPE

Long, long ago a giant named Maushope dwelt on the coast of Massachusetts. He waded between the shore and Martin Wyngaard's Island. The water did not come to his knees. But he did not like to get his feet wet, so he thought he would build a bridge. He began by putting down some stones between Cuttyhunk and Gay Head. Then a crab pinched one of his toes. That upset him so much that he could not finish the bridge.

One day when he was in a bad temper, he cut off a piece of Martin Wyngaard's Island. It is now called No Man's Land. Another time, when he was in a bad temper, he changed his children into fish. His wife tried to stop him. Then he threw her across the bay.

Some said he used to light false signal fires, to lead ships astray. Others said they were the fires by which he cooked his food. He pulled up trees by the roots and burned them. Then he broiled whales over the coals. There are great fields of lignite on Martin Wyngaard's Island to this day. They are from the giant Maushope's fires.

Some said he used to spread fogs to destroy ships. Others said, when they saw the fog rising, "Old Maushope is smoking his pipe." When he had finished smoking he always emptied his pipe in the same place. The ashes rose higher and higher. At last they rose above the water. They are there to this day, and have been named Nantucket.

Perhaps you can imagine the size of that ash pile when you know that 10,000 people once lived upon it. That was when the demand for whale oil was greatest, and whales were plentiful near our shores. Nantucket was the principal whaling port of this country.

THE DORCHESTER GIANT

Long, long ago there dwelt in Dorchester a giant. Once, when he was going away, he made a pudding for his children to eat while he was gone. He stuffed it with plums, as big as the golden dome on the Boston State House. When the children had eaten all they wished, they played with the rest of the pudding. They threw pieces of it all over Dorchester, Roxbury, and Milton. They fell as thick as hail. They lie there to this day, and people call them pudding-stone.

THE WHITE DEER OF ONOTA

When the white men came to this country the red men told them of a white deer which came to drink at Onota every spring, when the cherry trees were in bloom. It was always greeted with shouts of joy, for their wise men had once said, "As long

"He has to twist the sand into ropes, and shovel the waves back into the sea."—HARRY MAIN

"The ashes rose higher and higher. At last they rose above the water."—THE GIANT MAUSHOPE

"coaxed him . . . to shoot the white deer . . ."—THE WHITE DEER OF ONOTA

"He lifted one large rock and placed it on top of another." —BALANCED ROCK

as the white deer comes to drink at Onota the frost will not blight the crop, nor will the plague destroy our tribe, nor will enemies lay waste our land."

Once a messenger came to the tribe from the great province in the north. He heard the story of the white deer. Then he thought, "If I could lay that white skin before the feet of my king, when I return to France, and tell him the tale of the wonderful deer, I would be sure of great favor."

He went to the red men and offered a large sum of money to any person who would shoot the white deer. It was more money than any of them had ever had. But they refused in horror. The messenger saw that no amount of money would buy the skin of the white deer. He tried to think of some other way.

Among the red men was a brave named Wando. He was very fond of what the red men called fire-water. The messenger sent for Wando, and gave him so much of this that Wando was no longer himself. Then the messenger coaxed him, with the promise of still more firewater, to shoot the white deer and take off its skin.

After that they both hurried away. They wished to get out of the country as soon as possible. But when Wando once more became himself, he was overcome with anguish. He confessed his crime, and both he and his tempter were punished.

The red men sought to make peace with the gods by prayer and sacrifice. But from this time they became poorer and poorer.

BALANCED ROCK

Long, long ago a great chief dwelt at the place now called Pittsfield. He was one of the Atotarhos. They were the kings of the six nations. He was not fond of war, like so many other chiefs. He loved peace and was kind. He was small and frail looking. His voice was soft as that of a woman.

One day he was watching some boys at play. They were trying to see who was the strongest. They did not know Atotarhos. They did not think he could be very strong or brave. He was small and looked meek. They made fun of him. Then they asked him if he would like to try his strength against theirs. He agreed, and went forward.

At every step he grew larger. He became a giant. Now the boys understood who he was. They bowed humbly before him. He picked up stones so large that no one had ever thought of trying to move them. These he threw about as if they were nuts. He lifted one large rock and placed it on top of another.

Then he spoke to the boys. He told them never to be uncivil to strangers. He told them never to judge people whom they did not know. After he had finished speaking he changed, and became small and frail as before. For many years after, old men used to climb Balanced Rock and, standing there, tell the tale of Atotarhos and repeat his advice.

✷ ✷ ✷

Balanced Rock is eighteen feet high and weighs about one hundred fifty tons. It rests on one square foot of surface. A man standing on it can easily set it in motion.

THE WITCHES OF AGAWAM

Among the first settlers was a minister by the name of Thomas Hooker. Once he went on a journey, and in the evening he came to Agawam. Mr. Hooker wished to put up at the inn over night, but the host told him there was no room. He had only one room vacant, and that was haunted. But Mr. Hooker was a brave and a wise man. He was not afraid of ghosts or of anything else. He went to sleep in the haunted room.

At midnight he awoke. Then he saw a witch come in through the keyhole. Then another came through a crack in the floor. Another came through a crack in the wall. More and more kept coming, bringing with them gold and silver dishes.

At last the room was filled with witches, and they began to prepare a feast. When it was ready they asked Mr. Hooker to eat with them. He knew that anyone who eats with witches must also become a witch. Still he accepted, and sat down with them. But he told them that he never began to eat without first asking a blessing. Then he began the blessing, before anyone had had time to answer. Out flew the witches, so fast he could not see how or where they went. They left the food and all the costly dishes behind.

In the morning Mr. Hooker packed all the dishes together and put them on his horse. Then he mounted and rode on his way. A crow followed him, flapped about his head, and cawed. After a while it seemed to Mr. Hooker that her cries sounded like human words. He listened, and heard the crow say, "You are Hooker by name and hooker by nature."

✶　✶　✶

Thomas Hooker was the founder of Connecticut. He led a party of ninety pioneers from the settlements around Boston into the Connecticut valley in the fall of 1635. They built the log cabins which were the first homes of Hartford.

Agawam was settled soon after. The name was later changed to Springfield.

HARRY MAIN

Long, long ago there lived on the coast a man named Harry Main. He was a wicked man. He was a smuggler and a pirate. He used to light false signals. Thus he caused many ships to be wrecked.

Most of these ships perished at Ipswich bar. Therefore, when Harry was dead, he was doomed to receive his punishment there. He has to twist the sand into ropes, and shovel the waves back into the sea. But his ropes are always breaking, and the waves roll back against his shovel. When this happens he roars and screams with rage. Strangers think it is the storm howling, but the people of Ipswich say, when they hear the roar, "Now old Harry is grumbling."

When Harry Main makes a very long rope, he is allowed to rest awhile on Plum Island. Many believe it was there he hid the treasure which he took from the wrecked ships.

A man once dreamed that Harry Main's treasure was hidden in an old mill. He knew the mill very well. He had the same dream the second night. He had the same dream the third night. Then he thought he had better look for the treasure. He

waited until a very dark night. Then he went to
the mill. He took with him a lantern, a spade, and
a Bible. He found the place he had seen in his
dreams, and began to dig.

Soon he came to a large, flat stone. On the stone
lay an iron bar. The man took the bar and tried to
lift the stone with it. Then all at once he saw a
number of black cats with fiery eyes. They were
standing around the hole he had dug. The man

swung the iron bar and cried, "Scat." Then all the cats were gone. He could not tell what became of them. But at the same moment the hole was filled with ice-cold water. The man was standing in it up to his waist. When people heard of this they thought it best not to look for Harry Main's treasure.

Legend of Rhode Island

THE SINGER OF SEKONNET POINT

Long, long ago those who passed Sekonnet Point often heard the sound of sweet singing. It came from the shore. Many a fisherman moored his boat and went to find the singer. Then he discovered that it was the Giant Maushope's wife. He had thrown her across Buzzards Bay when she tried to stop him from changing their children into fish, and she fell at this place.

There she sat for years and years, gazing out over the water and singing sad songs. She demanded payment of all who came to hear her. In spite of this, many came back as often as they could. They wished to hear the wonderful song. One day they listened for it in vain. At last one man went ashore to see what had become of the singer. He found her at the same place, but she had turned to stone.

Dick West

Legends of Connecticut

LEGEND OF LAKE MASHAPAUG

Long, long ago the Narragansett and the Nipmuck tribes dwelt in Connecticut. Once the Narragansetts invited the Nipmucks to visit them. The Narragansetts lived by the sea, and they gave their guests fish to eat. Then the Nipmucks invited the Narrangansetts for a visit. Their land was rich, and they raised corn. Their woods were full of game. They gave their guests corn and venison to eat. But the Nipmucks began to quarrel with their guests. The quarrel grew into a fight. Many were killed on both sides. The Nipmucks buried the guests whom they had killed, but no grass ever grew on their graves.

The Nipmuck god was angry with his people because they had treated their guests so badly. He decided to punish them. One day the whole tribe gathered in a beautiful wooded valley, to hold a feast and a council. Then the god pushed away the pillars of earth. The valley sank. The place was filled with water, and all the people were drowned. The place is filled with water to this day, and is called Lake Mashapaug.

Among the Nipmucks there was one very good old woman. The ground remained firm under her feet. That place is called Loon Island.

* * *

Until recent years the remains of a forest have been visible on the bottom of Lake Mashapaug.

THE NEW HAVEN GHOST SHIP

In the days of the first settlers a ship once sailed out from New Haven. It was in the midst of winter. The harbor was frozen over. The ice had to be cut for several miles before the ship could get through. Many thought it would never come back, and it never did. No one ever saw or heard of the ship again.

One day, six months later, a ship came sailing into the harbor just after a rain. It was going against the wind, and it neither rose nor fell with the waves. The water did not ripple around it. All its sails were set. Those who saw it thought it looked just like the lost ship. No one could be seen on board at first. When the ship came nearer one man was seen. He pointed out toward the sea. All at once masts and sails fell together. The ship sank, without disturbing the water as it went down. The New Haven people thought it had been sent to show them what had become of their ship.

"On and on went the wolves, higher and higher up into the mountains."—CHIEF PASSA-CONAWAY

" 'Wasawa is coming. Wasawa is back.' "—THE INVENTION OF SNOW SHOES

"At the same moment the rock from which the stone hung loosened."—THE GREAT RUBY

"Every time the fly bit he stamped his feet."—THE FALLS IN THE MERRIMAC

"They kidnapped them and gave them fairy bread to eat." —THE FAIRIES IN THE AGIOCHOOKS

"In the darkness of night she carried out her purpose." —CHIEF PEMIGEWASSET

Legends of New Hampshire

THE FALLS IN THE MERRIMAC

When the world was new the ground was flat, and the Merrimac flowed quietly between smooth pastures. One day a moose came to the river to drink. In those days the moose was so large that a man, standing on another man's shoulders, could hardly have looked over his back. The moose was very thirsty, and he drank and drank. The water in the river began to sink. A beaver was building his home in the river bank, and he became uneasy. He was afraid the water would sink below his house.

The beaver sent his children to the woods to ask the other animals to come and drive the moose away. But the animals in the woods did not care if the river sank, and, besides, they were all afraid of the moose, so they all made excuses. The bear was too sleepy.

The wolf had to go away. The fox was busy. But the moose kept on drinking, and the water sank lower and lower.

The fish became uneasy. They were afraid there would not be enough water to swim in. One of them saw a fly, sailing down the river on a leaf. In times of great trouble help is sought everywhere, so the fish called, "Little fly, can't you drive the moose away?"

"I can try," answered the fly. "I am not afraid of the moose. I am not afraid of any animals, no matter how big they are."

And the fly flew up to the moose, lighted on his foreleg, and began to bite. The moose stamped his foot, but the fly only bit a little harder.

"Let me be," he bellowed, "or I shall crush you under my hoofs."

The fly laughed. Then she bit a little harder. She kept on until the moose was beside himself. He began to run along the river bank. Every time the fly bit he stamped his feet. Every time the moose stamped his feet the ground sank. The water rushed and tumbled

over all the steep places he made, and that is why there are so many falls in the Merrimac.

The Indians gave several names to this river. One of them was Kaskaashadi, meaning "Broken Waters." The early French explorers visited it, and the sagas of the Northmen describe a river which was probably the Merrimac. But the English were the first who settled on its bank.

Because of the great water power of the Merrimac, many towns were located on its banks. It was said that the Merrimac turned more machinery than any other river in the world.

CHIEF PASSACONAWAY

Long, long ago the Pennacook Indians had a wise and powerful chief. His name was Passaconaway. He was a prophet, and he could work magic. He could make water burn. He could make the rocks move. He could make the trees dance. He could make an empty snakeskin crawl about. He could change himself into a burning fire.

When the palefaces came there was among them a good man named John Eliot. He has been called "the Apostle of the Red Men." He talked to Passaconaway about the God of the white people. The chief listened to his teaching, and believed in his God. After that he would no longer work magic.

When Passaconaway had lived a hundred years and one score more, he left his people and lived alone. One night a pack of wolves ran over Lake Winnepesaukee, drawing a sled. On the sled stood a throne, covered with furs. The wolves stopped before the dwelling of the old chief. He came out, climbed into the sled, and seated himself on the throne. The wolves ran on, across the lake, through woods, over ravines, and up mountain slopes. The old chief was singing his death song, and the tones echoed against the cliffs.

On and on went the wolves, higher and higher up into the mountains. At last they could be seen going up the highest peak. The sled was now on fire, so that the watchers could see it clearly. When the wolves came to the very top of the peak they left the sled and ran away, howling, into the darkness. But the burning sled rose among the stars and disappeared.

The Indians believed that every great sachem had some degree of power to work magic.

When the white settlers came, Passaconaway lived where the city of Lowell now is. Here he had his capital. He was friendly to the white people, and advised peace.

A statute of Passaconaway stands in Edson Cemetery, Lowell, Mass. It is not known when or where he died.

The wedding of his daughter is described by Whittier in "Bridal of Pennacook."

THE AGIOCHOOKS

When the world was new a red man once went out hunting. He roamed the country for many days, but did not find any game. Neither did he find anything else he could eat. He became faint from hunger, and very weary. At last he could go no farther. He sank down upon the ground, and thought that he would die. And he was so worn out and discouraged that he was glad to think he would die.

He fell asleep, and had a dream. He saw a beautiful land where fruit grew in plenty and there were animals and birds to shoot. But when he awoke he was still in this cold, desolate world. He became yet more discouraged, and cried out, asking where this wonderful land was that he had seen.

Then the Master of Life appeared to him and gave him a glowing coal. The man took it and dropped it on the ground. A great fire started from the piece of coal. The smoke rose and hid all the land. Out of the smoke came a voice like thunder. It bade the mountains rise. Then the earth trembled and opened. The man saw great rocks rise from within it. They heaped themselves, one on top of the other, until some were above the clouds. From the very highest peak came

a voice which said, "Here will the Great Spirit dwell, that He may watch over His children."

In time the mountains became covered with forests, and the red men named them the Agiochooks. They found game plentiful there, and made them their hunting grounds, but very few ever scaled the great height which the Great Spirit had chosen for His own. Those who did so never returned, but were doomed to wander over the highest peaks and through the darkest chasms for untold years. Their cries of despair could be heard in the winter storms.

*   *   *

The Agiochooks are known to us as the White Mountains.

For a long time the white settlers believed what the Indians told them about the unhappy spirits in the mountains. Hunters and exploring parties that were lost in the mountains sometimes returned with tales of great suffering, and with weird stories about things they had seen and heard. This strengthened the belief. In 1784, the ministers of Conway were asked to ex-

orcise the spirits that moaned so pitifully on stormy nights.

THE FAIRIES IN THE AGIOCHOOKS

Long, long ago the fairies had a meeting place near a rippling waterfall in the mountains. There they danced on the soft moss in the moonlight. They were very fond of little children. They kidnapped them and gave them fairy bread to eat. Then the children became small, like the fairies. After that they stayed and danced with them, so that most of those fairies were really little Indian children. When the palefaces came the fairies moved away, farther into the Agiochooks.

CHIEF PEMIGEWASSET

Long, long ago there dwelt in the Agiochooks a brave tribe, whose chief was the great and noble Pemigewasset. At one time they were attacked by the Mohawks. The battle lasted throughout the day and far into the night, so that the setting sun and the rising moon turned red, as they always did at the sight of warfare.

At last the Mohawks were conquered and fled. Pemigewasset and his men pursued them over mountains and hills, through valleys and streams. When they were tired out Pemigewasset told them to lie down and sleep, and when they were rested they would take up the chase once more.

But the wily Mohawks had been waiting for this. They returned and captured Pemigewasset and all his men while they slept. Then they carried them off to their village on the bank of the Shatemuc. All the tribe rejoiced to think the great Pemigewasset was their prisoner.

The Mohawk chief had a daughter, Minerwa. When she came to look at the prisoners Pemigewasset saw what a beautiful maiden she was. Minerwa read admiration in his eyes. Pemigewasset was as handsome as he was brave, and Minerwa thought what a pity it would be to put such a man to death. She found an opportunity to speak to Pemigewasset alone, and offered to set him free. But Pemigewasset refused to escape and leave all his men prisoners. Then Minerwa promised to help them all escape.

In the darkness of night she carried out her purpose. Pemigewasset asked her to follow him and become his bride. Minerwa knew that when the tribe discovered what she had done, her life would be taken in punishment, so she promised. They were to meet at a given place three days later. Before she went Minerwa pushed her canoe out into the stream and turned it over.

In the morning the prisoners were missed, and when the old chief discovered that his daughter also was missing, he thought he knew how they had escaped, and he felt very sad. But later her canoe was found, floating upside down in the water. Then it was believed that she had been drowned, and all the tribe mourned.

When Pemigewasset and his warriors returned to their people there was great rejoicing, and everyone felt grateful to Minerwa, and loved her for what she had done. A great wedding feast was prepared, and after that Pemigewasset and Minerwa lived happily for many years.

Then the Hurons went on the warpath, and attacked Pemigewasset and his tribe. They were also defeated and put to flight, but Pemigewasset was badly wounded. When Minerwa heard this she hurried to his side.

One of the Hurons, who had once visited the Mohawk village, saw and recognized her. He now journeyed to the village once more, and told the old chief where he had seen his daughter. The Mohawk chief was now very feeble, and could not make the long journey into the Agiochooks. But he sent one of his sons to ask Minerwa to visit him, that he might see her once more. He promised that if Pemigewasset would come with her no harm should befall him. The old chief no longer had any hard feelings against him. He had not long to live, and wished to make his peace with everyone.

Pemigewasset had been too badly wounded to do this, but he said, "Minerwa must go to visit her sick father. From the high mountain Pemigewasset will watch for her return."

When Minerwa had gone some of the men carried Pemigewasset to the top of the high mountain. He stayed there, and his people visited him, brought him food, and made him comfortable.

Each day Minerwa made a fire that sent the smoke high in the air, so that Pemigewasset could see it from the mountain. That was her greeting to him. When Pemigewasset saw the smoke from Minerwa's signal fire, he hastened to make a fire in the same way, to answer Minerwa's greeting. Every day Minerwa's signal fire was a little farther away. At last it was no longer seen. Then Pemigewasset knew she was near her father's village.

Minerwa saw and talked with her father. Soon after he went to sleep in her arms, and did not awake. When the funeral was over Minerwa set out for her home, and her brother went with her.

Among the Mohawks there was a man who had once wished to make Minerwa his wife. When he saw that she was alive, and happy, he was filled with a desire for revenge. He followed her and her brother in secret, and killed them both.

On the high mountain Pemigewasset began to wait for the fire that should tell of Minerwa's return. He watched for it from daybreak until dark. His wound was making him weaker, and his people begged him to come down, but he always answered, "When the smoke from Minerwa's fire tells of her return, then shall Pemigewasset come down, but not before."

He stayed there through the heat of the summer and the cold of the winter. At last the Great Spirit took pity on Pemigewasset and sent him a heavy sleep. When he awoke he was with Minerwa.

After that the Great Spirit bade the winds and the rains carve the image of Pemigewasset on the mountain where he had kept his faithful watch. It is there to this day, and we call it The Great Stone Face.

THE GREAT RUBY

Long, long ago a great ruby hung near the summit of Mount Monroe. It was suspended from a rock. In front of it was a deep ravine. All around it were jutting rocks. In the daytime it shone with a light that could be seen for miles. At night the rocks glowed with the light.

Many tried to get the precious stone, but no one ever got near enough. It was guarded by a spirit. After the palefaces came, many of them also tried to get it. Once a large party climbed the mountain. They took with them a wise man who, they thought, could drive away the guarding spirit. They returned without the stone, and they had been "sorely buffeted."

One man spent his whole life trying to get the great ruby. When he had become old and gray he went up the mountain with some friends. He climbed ahead of the others. They saw him get so near the stone that it seemed he could touch it. Then they saw him sink down. His arms were still stretched out toward the stone. At the same moment the rock from which the stone hung loosened. It began to roll down. Flames rose from the rocks it struck. At last it rolled into the Lake of the Clouds. A bright light sometimes shines through the water of this lake. In the darkness of night Mount Monroe often glows dull red.

THE INVENTION OF SNOW SHOES

Laughing Eyes was the daughter of a chief. Two young braves of the tribe loved her. One was Wasawa, whom Laughing Eyes and all the tribe liked. The other was Oakana, whom the chief liked better. But the chief did not wish to make his daughter unhappy, and tried to find some way to induce her to marry Oakana.

At last he thought of a plan. He had a message to send to a chief in the far North. He told the two young men that he would prepare two messages and let them take one each. The one who first returned with the reply should have his daughter.

It would be a difficult journey. The snow lay deep, and there were no blazed trees to show the way. But the lovers joyfully consented, each one feeling sure that he would be successful.

When Wasawa came to see Laughing Eyes her eyes were not laughing. They were sad, for she knew he was not as strong as Oakana. But Wasawa assured her that he felt sure of winning in the long race. Oakana also came to see Laughing Eyes, and told her to prepare for the wedding while he was gone, for they would be married as soon as he returned.

The next night Laughing Eyes had a dream. She saw ducks walking on top of the snow. Then she awoke. After a while she fell asleep again, and dreamed that she saw ducks walking on top of the snow. Then she awoke. After a while she fell asleep again, and dreamed that she saw ducks walking on top of the snow, while other birds sank down into it. Laughing Eyes had been taught to believe in dreams, and she wondered what this could mean.

She thought it must have something to do with the journey her suitors were to take.

Every morning Laughing Eyes scattered some food for the birds in front of her wigwam. Two ducks had stayed all winter, instead of flying south with the others. They came to feed with the other birds, and were so tame that Laughing Eyes could go close up to them. She caught one of the ducks and threw it far out over the snow. The duck ran back to her. She did this several times, and the duck ran back, as if they were playing a game. Laughing Eyes caught another bird and threw it, but this bird sank down into the snow, and she had to go to its rescue. Her dream had come true.

Laughing Eyes looked at the feet of the birds, and realized that it was the web between the toes of the duck that enabled it to walk on the snow. She went into the wigwam, and sat down to think. After a while she got out a roll of soft deer skin. Then she hunted up some pliable strips of ash which her father used for making· bows. She cut thongs out of the skins, then bent a strip of wood into a frame, and fastened it firmly together. She laced the thongs of skin back and forth to cover it. Then she tied on others to be used in fastening the strange shoe. The second one was far easier to make than the first.

When Wasawa came that evening she told him her dream and showed him the shoes which she believed would serve the same purpose as the web feet of the duck. Wasawa was amused at first, then, when he saw how serious Laughing Eyes was, he became disgusted. But she pleaded with him until he promised to take the queer looking objects, and try them. She also asked him not to show them to anyone, or let Oakana see him put them on. This he promised very willingly, for he felt sure that if they were seen both he and Laughing Eyes would be ridiculed.

In a few days the chief had prepared the two messages, each painted on a roll of birch bark. The two young men set out at the same time, side by side. All the tribe watched them depart, and all wished that Wasawa might win, but did not think it likely.

The second day it began to snow, and walking became very difficult. Oakana, strong and sturdy, soon left his comrade far behind. Now Wasawa took out the snow shoes, which he carried on his back, wrapped in a skin. He put them on, tried to take a step, and fell. He got up, tried again, and fell. He was angry, but he had promised Laughing Eyes not to throw them away until he had given them a fair trial. He chose a tree some distance away, and decided to wear them until he reached it. It took a long while, and he had many falls, but by the time he arrived at his goal he realized that he had not once sunk down in the deep, soft snow. Perhaps there was some merit to this, after all. He kept on, and soon found it easier to keep his footing. Faster and faster he walked. He began to run, and by sundown he was pretending that he raced with the birds in the air.

One evening at sunset Wasawa approached the village where he was to deliver his message. He easily recognized the chief's tent. The chief was sitting outside watching the sunset, which cast a glow over the bright snow. He took the roll from Wasawa, but did not look at it. He looked only at the feet of the messenger. By and by all the tribe came to look at the feet of the stranger. They forgot the red man's custom of not asking questions or betraying curiosity, and Wasawa had to explain how and where he got his strange shoes.

He rested a few days while the chief prepared the answer to his message. When he departed, it seemed to him that the whole tribe followed him— on snow shoes. The squaws had been very busy copying his shoes.

One day the father of Laughing Eyes heard the call, "Wasawa is coming. Wasawa is back."

The chief smiled. He knew Wasawa would have done well to reach the village in the north by this time. But soon the young man entered his wigwam, and announced that he had brought back the answer from the chief in the north. The chief thought, at first, that Wasawa was trying to deceive him, but when he saw the pictures on the roll of bark he knew that Wasawa told the truth, and he gave orders for the preparation of a grand wedding feast.

When Oakana arrived at the village in the North he was told that the same message had been brought, and the answer taken back, many days ago by a man who had wings on his feet.

THE
Central
and
Southern
Atlantic
STATES

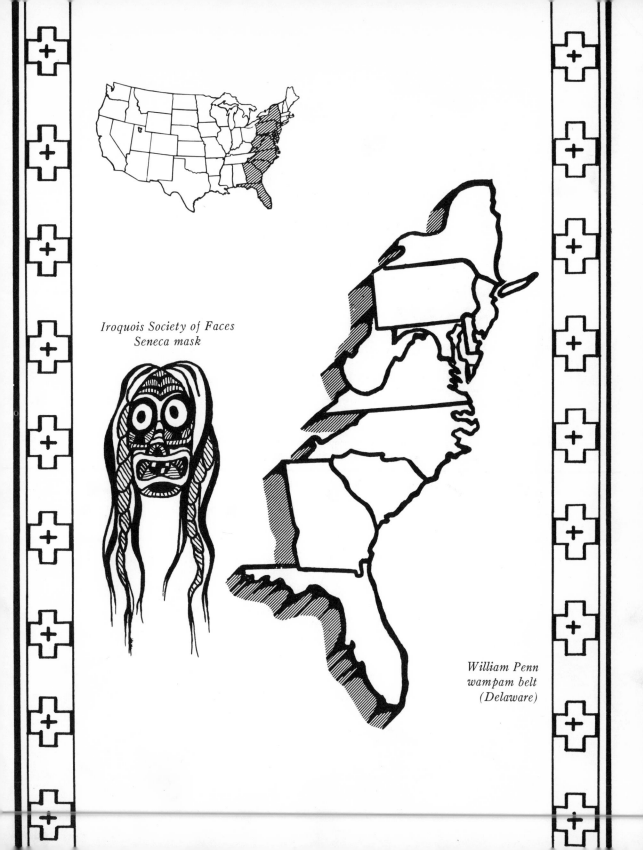

Iroquois Society of Faces
Seneca mask

William Penn
wampam belt
(Delaware)

Legends of North Carolina

THE NUNNEHI

Long, long ago the Nunnehi dwelt in the mountains. They loved the high, bare peaks, where no trees ever grow. Sometimes when the red men went hunting in the mountains they heard the sound of a drum, and of singing and dancing. If they tried to follow the sound they would hear it in another direction. No matter how long they tried, they never could get sight of the dancers. Then they knew it was the Nunnehi they heard.

The Nunnehi liked the red men and were friendly. Sometimes they changed themselves, so as to look and act like them. Then they would join their company, and the red men never knew that Nunnehi were with them.

Once a boy was playing near a river, not far from

home. A strange man came and spoke to him. When they had talked a while the stranger asked the boy to come home with him. He said he would give the boy something good to eat. The boy went with him, and he met many people whom he had never seen before. They all seemed glad to see him, and were very kind.

The boy played with the children and had a very good time. They wanted him to stay all night. A man who lived near the boy came and spoke to him. He was sure the neighbor would tell his parents where he was, so he stayed. In the morning one of the men said he would show him the way home.

They went down a trail the boy had never seen before. On one side of it was a peach orchard. On the other side was a cornfield. Soon they came to another trail. Then the man showed the boy which way he was to go, and left him. But the boy turned to look after the man. He did not see him. He did not see the trail. He did not see the orchard. He did not see the cornfield. All he could see was the mountain slope, and the trees that grew there.

The boy was frightened and puzzled, but he thought he had better follow the trail the man had pointed out. In a little while he came home. There he saw everyone very much excited. They thought he had either been drowned, or killed in the mountains. Men had been searching for him all night. The boy said he had thought the neighbor he had spoken to would tell his parents where he was. Then the neighbor came forward and said, "I have not seen you or spoken to you. I have been looking for you all night, too."

Now the boy's father asked him to tell exactly where he had been and what had happened. When they heard it they knew he had been with the Nunnehi.

THE LITTLE PEOPLE

Long, long ago the Little People dwelt in the black caves of the Smoky Hill Mountains. They could hardly reach to the knee of a grown man. They were very pretty, and had long hair that hung down to the ground.

The Little People loved music. Most of the time they were playing the drum and dancing. If a hunter heard the sound of a drum in the woods it was better not to follow it. It might be the Little People. They were very mischievous. If a hunter, when he came home, looked and acted as if he did not know where

he was or where he had been, then his friends knew he had met the Little People, and they had thrown a spell over him.

If a hunter found a knife in the woods, he had to be careful. It might belong to the Little People. If he said, "Little People, I want to take this knife," they did not hurt him. But if he took it and did not say anything, they threw stones at him.

If there was a sound of talking about the house at night, it was better not to go out. It might be the Little People. It could be seen in the morning if they had been there. Then the corn would be gathered, or the fields would be cleared.

THE DETSATA

Hunters also had to look out for the pranks of the Detsata. Detsata was a boy who ran away from home. He went to the woods, where he lived ever after, and he had many children. They all looked alike, and were called the Detsata.

Sometimes a flock of birds would get frightened and fly up, and the hunter could not tell what had scared them. Then he knew the Detsata were chasing them. If the hunter shot his arrow into a clear space, and then could not find it, he knew the Detsata were hiding it. Then he would say, "Detsata, if you do not give up my arrow I shall scratch you." Then he would look once more, and this time he would find it.

THE GIANTS' GARDEN

When the world was new the great Atlantic Ocean went all the way up to the mountains. Some giants dwelt in the mountains. They wished to make a garden. They were very fond of corn. They liked rice and sweet potatoes and other vegetables, too. They needed cotton to make clothes for their children, and they thought it would be nice to raise sugar-cane to make candy for them.

But they wanted to have the garden on the side where the sea was, so that they would not have to carry water over the mountains. There was not enough land on that side, so the giants thought the best way would be to lift up some of the land that was under the sea.

They all stood in a row and began to lift very, very slowly. But the land under the sea was loose and soft, mostly sand, and when the giants had got it up pretty high it broke all the way across, and the part that was farthest from them fell, until the outside edge was in the water. When it struck the water it crumbled and broke into many small pieces, and the water rushed in between them. Then the giants thought they had better leave it just as it was.

After a while they were just as well pleased, for they found that many of the things they wished to raise grew better down on the low land than they would have done where the giants had intended to

"... when the giants had got it up pretty high it broke all the way across ..."—THE GIANTS' GARDEN

"... the stranger asked the boy to come home with him."—THE NUNNEHI

"Most of the time they were playing the drum and dancing."—THE LITTLE PEOPLE

plant them. And when they lifted the land it had cracked in many places, and now the water stayed in those cracks, forming rivers that gave them plenty of water for their garden.

When the giant children went to play by the sea they had a good time skipping on the broken-off pieces of land, just as human children skip on the stones in a brook.

Legends of Virginia

THE BRIDGE OF THE GREAT SPIRIT

Long, long ago the Mohegans once went on the warpath. They were defeated and had to run away. They came to a ravine, which they thought must be bottomless. They could go no further, and behind them was the enemy, getting nearer every moment. The medicine men told them to pray. They did so, and when they looked up again there was a bridge over the ravine. When they saw that the Great Spirit had listened to their prayers and wished to help them, their courage returned. They let the women and children pass over the bridge, but the men stayed to await the enemy. When they came the Mohegans fought and conquered. The bridge was named The Bridge of the Great Spirit, but the palefaces called it Natural Bridge.

"... when they looked up
again there was a bridge over
the ravine."—THE BRIDGE OF
THE GREAT SPIRIT

Dick West

$\ast$ $\ast$ $\ast$

A road has been made across the bridge. It is fenced and has a border of trees and bushes. People have sometimes passed over it without knowing how high they were above the stream which flows at the bottom of the ravine.

CLIP

Long, long ago, when people believed in witches, there was a house in the state of Virginia which was supposed to be inhabited by them. The house was by the roadside, and if anyone passed at night the witches would rush out and clip pieces from his clothing. Hence the place became known as Clip, and it is so called to this day.

Legends of Pennsylvania

THE LEGEND OF MAUCH CHUNK

When the world was new there was a sparkling lake where the city of Mauch Chunk is now. It had many bays. On the prettiest of these some Lenni Lenape Indians had built a village.

Among them was a young chief named Onoko. He was a large, fine looking man. He was very strong and very brave. All alone he had fought and killed a bear on the mountain, which was then named Mauch Chunk —Bear Mountain. Onoko was rich. His wigwam was the largest and best furnished. He was betrothed to the fairest maiden of the tribe, whose name was Winona—the first born.

One day they were floating about on the lake in their canoe. Then Manitou rose above the mountain. He envied Onoko all his good fortune. Now, when he

saw the lovers, his face grew dark with hatred. Lightning flashed from his eyes. Thunder roared about his head. He drew onto his right hand his magic mitten. Then he struck the earth. The mountains shook and split open. The lake streamed through the opening. It carried off the canoe. Onoko and his bride were buried in the water. The lake streams through the opening to this day. It is called Lehigh River.

✷ ✷ ✷

A cascade and a pretty glen near Mauch Chunk have been named for Chief Onoko.

THE GIANT TURTLE

Long, long ago this world was a place of peace, happiness, and prosperity. War and strife were unknown. No one died until he had attained a very great age. Then evil beings entered the world, and taught some of its people sorcery. They began to kill their fellow men, and perform other cruel deeds. The wicked became constantly more numerous, until it seemed as if there would be no good people left. At last a great flood was sent to destroy them. It covered all the earth, and only a few people were left alive. These saved themselves by climbing upon the back of a giant turtle. This turtle was so old that its back had become mossy. The people saw a loon floating on the water. They called to him, and asked him to dive below the water and bring up a little land. The loon

"... his face grew dark with hatred. Lightning flashed from his eyes."—THE LEGEND OF MAUCH CHUNK

"These saved themselves by climbing upon the back of a giant turtle."—THE GIANT TURTLE

"Woksis had ... set a kettle below this to catch the sap." —THE DISCOVERY OF MAPLE SUGAR

Dick West

tried again and again, but the water was too deep. At last he was able to find the earth, and came up with some of it in his bill. This the people mixed with the moss on the turtle's back. They tended it very carefully, and it kept growing larger. At last there was a new earth, and it was peopled by the children of those who saved themselves from the flood. The earth still rests on the back of the giant turtle. When the turtle moves there are earthquakes and floods.

THE DISCOVERY OF MAPLE SUGAR

The brave Woksis was going out hunting. He made a mark in the snow near a high rock and told his wife, Moqua, that he would return when the sun had reached that mark. Moqua knew that he would be tired and hungry, and she must have a meal prepared when he came.

When she thought it about time, Moqua made a fire, filled a kettle with snow, and set it over the fire.

When the snow had melted and boiled, she put a piece of meat into it. Then she went into the wigwam and sat down to her beadwork.

When Moqua came out to look after her cooking she found that the kettle had fallen over, and the water had poured out and put out the fire. But the meat lay unharmed in the kettle.

Moqua hastened to make a new fire. Then she looked toward the mark Woksis had made in the snow. The sun was very near it. To gather fresh snow and melt it would take a long while. What was she to do?

Close by the wigwam stood a maple, in which the sap had begun to run, for it was early spring. Woksis had bored a hole in the trunk of the tree and set a kettle below this to catch the sap, for he was very fond of this. Moqua emptied the contents of this kettle into the one she used for cooking, and when the sap began to boil she put the meat into it. When Woksis returned his dinner was ready. Moqua took out the meat, and set the kettle in the snow to cool. The meat had an unusual flavor, and Woksis was pleased. He told Moqua she had cooked it better than ever before.

When Moqua went out to get her kettle, she found the sap turned into a yellowish substance, like sand. She wondered if this would have happened if there had been no meat cooked in it. She emptied and washed the kettle, then poured into it the small quantity of sap that had gathered in the kettle by the tree, boiled it, and set it in the snow to cool. The result was maple sugar, such as we all enjoy every spring. From that time the red men made maple sugar every spring, and the fame of Moqua's skill in cooking went from tribe to tribe.

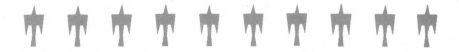

Legends of New York

LEGEND OF THE IROQUOIS

Before there were any people on the earth the red men dwelt under the ground. The Holder of the Heavens brought them out. Then he led them toward the rising sun. When they came to the Shatemuc he let one nation make its home there. The others he led back, and gave four nations their homes between the Shatemuc and the Great Lakes. He taught them to hunt and to prepare their food. He taught them to make clothes and to build houses. Two other nations came out of the earth with them. These the Holder of the Heavens led into other lands.

✳   ✳   ✳

The Iroquois have been called the Five Nations of New York. They were strong and powerful. They built long houses, and many families lived in each house, but they did not live together. There was a space divided off for each family. In the same way each tribe had its separate part of the land. Therefore they called their territory the long house. The Mohawks, who lived by the Shatemuc, were called the keepers of the eastern door. The Seneca lived by Lake Erie. They were keepers of the western door.

THE FINGER LAKES

Long, long ago a giant dwelt in the country south of the Great Lakes. The land was flat, and the giant wished to have some low places where he could get water. He spread open the fingers of one hand, and pressed them against the ground so hard that they made hollow places. These hollows became filled with water, just as the giant had expected. They are full of water to this day, and we call them the Finger Lakes.

LEGEND OF LAKE ONEIDA

When the Great Spirit had finished making the world, he looked down upon it. His glance fell on Lake Oneida, and he smiled. Then Frenchman's Island rose out of the water. When the Great Spirit saw that he laughed aloud. Then Lotus Island rose to the surface to listen to his voice.

THE FIRST MOSQUITO

Long, long ago a giant mosquito lived near Lake Onondaga. When he was hungry he ate red men. They had no weapons that could hurt him. They asked the Holder of the Heavens to help them. He came down to destroy the mosquito, but it flew away so fast he could hardly keep it in sight. First it flew all around Lake Erie. Then it flew to Green Lake. There were witches at that lake, and the mosquito thought they would help him. When the witches would not help him, the mosquito flew to Lake Onondaga. There the

"Under the ground dwelt an evil spirit. It looked like a long serpent."—LEGEND OF NIAGARA

"She was placed in a white canoe . . . and sent over the falls."—THE MAID OF THE MIST

Dick West

". . . the owl fell down, dead. A white dove rose out of her body."—LEGEND OF SARATOGA

". . . a beautiful red flower was found . . . where Lenawee had shed her own blood . . ."—THE BLOOD OF LENAWEE

Holder of the Heavens caught up with him and killed him. The mosquito struggled so hard that the sand around the lake was piled up in high hills. Its blood was sprinkled over the earth, and from this came all small mosquitoes.

THE PET SNAKE

Long, long ago the red men who dwelt near Lake Canandaigua caught a pretty spotted snake. They did not kill it. They took it to their camp and kept it for a pet.

The snake grew and grew. It became so large that it lay curled all around the camp. It would eat a deer in one meal. It also became vicious. Even its keepers were afraid of it. Many arrows were shot at the snake, but they did not go through his thick skin. No one dared go near enough to kill it in any other way.

At last a boy made an arrow of red willow. This he dipped into the blood of a young squaw. Then he shot it at the snake. It went through the skin, but at first it did not seem to hurt. But the arrow went in deeper and deeper. The snake began to twist and roll about. At last it rolled into the lake and was drowned.

THE BLOOD OF LENAWEE

At one time a sickness came upon the red people. They called it the Quick Death. It took away old and young. One of the first to go was the Arrow, so named for his speed in running.

The people made sacrifices, but the sickness continued. At last one of their prophets went up on a high mountain to talk with the Great Spirit. When he returned he told them the Great Spirit was angry because of their sins. Nothing but human sacrifice would take away his wrath.

There was among them a maiden named Lenawee. Had the Arrow lived, she would have become his bride. She came forward and offered to sacrifice herself for

her people. She no longer wished to live, since her beloved had gone out of life. The next morning a beautiful red flower was found growing on the shady bank where Lenawee had shed her own blood for her people.

The red men made a feast in honor of the flower. It became to them the symbol of unselfishness. They named it The Blood of Lenawee, but the white people call it Indian Plume.

LEGEND OF NIAGARA

Long, long ago the god of clouds and rain had his abode under Oniagarah. His name was Hinun. His wigwam was behind the falling waters.

Under the ground dwelt an evil spirit. It looked like a long serpent. At one time it brought sickness to the red men. Many of them died. Then Hinun struck the evil spirit with lightning. It came up and floated down between the rocks. It twisted and squirmed with pain. The rocks bent as it pushed its great twisting body against them. They are bent to this day.

THE MAID OF THE MIST

The red men believed that a mighty spirit, whose voice was the sound of the cataract, dwelt in Oniagarah. He required two human sacrifices each year, and one of them had to be a maiden. She was placed in a white canoe filled with flowers and fruit, and sent over the falls. The one who was chosen was glad to go, for it was an honor. It was believed that she would become the bride of Manitou, and receive great honor in the next world also.

The last maiden to be sacrificed was Lelawala. She was the daughter of Chief Eagle Eye. When he saw her boat caught in the current, Eagle Eye found that he could not bear to sacrifice his daughter. He hurried out in his own canoe to save her. But it was too late. Both canoes went down in the current, and Eagle Eye was sacrificed with his daughter. Then they were changed into spirits of strength and goodness. They dwell in a crystal cave beneath the Falls. The sound of the water is to them like the sweetest music. Lelawala's name was changed to Maid of the Mist.

✳   ✳   ✳

The name Maid of the Mist has been given to the little boat that takes people up close to the cataract.

The sacrifice of Lelawala was witnessed by La Salle, the explorer. He tried, with all his eloquence, to prevent it, but it was in vain.

THE STONE GIANTS

Long, long ago some of the red men from the west came to the Mississippi. The river was overgrown with vines. They began to cross on the vines. But these broke, so most of them had to stay on the other side. Those who had crossed wandered about the Great

Lakes until they came to Oniagarah. They killed and ate the red men they found there. Every day they rolled themselves in the sand. This made their bodies hard as stone. Then they were called Stone Giants.

When the Holder of the Heavens heard of the misdeeds of the Stone Giants, he changed himself so that he looked like one of them. Then he went to them and said he would lead them to a country that was better than this. He took them to a valley, not far from Lake Onondaga. Then he went up on a high hill. From there he threw down rocks on the giants. He killed all but one. That one fled to the North.

SIR WILLIAM'S DREAMLAND TRACT

Sir William Johnson was Indian Commissioner of New York. He was always very cordial to the Indians, and they were his friends.

One of the Mohawk chiefs, King Hendrick, liked to dress like the white people. One day he came to Sir William and said, "I dream."

"Did you? What did you dream?" asked Sir William.

"I dream my white brother give me one suit of clothes."

Sir William answered, "Then I suppose you must have it."

A few days after that they met in the woods, and Sir William said, "I dreamed last night."

"What did my white brother dream?" asked King Hendrick.

"I dreamed King Hendrick gave me a tract of land on the Mohawk." And Sir William described a fine piece of land.

King Hendrick thought a while. "Then you must have it," he said. "But my white brother must never dream again."

$$\star \quad \star \quad \star$$

At one time Sir William was very sick. The Indians had a Medicine Spring which the Great Spirit had given to them. They had never let any white man know about it. Now they held a council to decide if they had not better tell Sir William, and let him have the benefit of it. They agreed to do so, and some of the Indians went to the spring and built a bark lodge for Sir William.

The spring was in the deep forest, and no road led to it, except a trail made by hunters. The Indians took him as far as they could in a boat. After that they carried him on their shoulders in a litter.

When they came to the spring, there were many ceremonies to be performed before Sir William could be allowed to use the sacred water. He had time to stay only a few days, but when he returned he was well enough to walk part of the way. The spring was named Saratoga. It still has its healing qualities, and many go there every year to be cured of illness.

LEGEND OF SARATOGA

A young Mohawk once went to hunt in the woods about Saratoga. It was late in the fall. Nearly all the leaves were gone, and it was starting to snow. The hunter lost his way. He wandered about for many days, but he could not find his way out of the woods or find anything to eat.

The hunter grew weak from hunger. He was also in great fear, for the red men believed that a lost person was led about in a circle by an evil spirit. The circle got smaller and smaller, and when the lost one came to the center of it he met death.

One day, as the shadows were falling, the hunter saw a large gray owl fly across his path. Then she rested in an old tree that had been killed by lightning, and began to call, "To whoo— To whoo—." The hunter thought this must be the evil spirit that had been leading him around, and that it was now making fun of him. Gathering all the strength he had left, he lifted his bow and shot an arrow at the owl. She fell down, dead. A white dove rose out of her body and flew just in front of the hunter. At the same time the moon shone down between the trees. The hunter followed the white dove, and soon he came to a trail he knew.

THE ADIRONDACKS

Long, long ago two tribes of red men went on the warpath. One was defeated, and took refuge in its own hunting grounds. But now the warriors were too weak and discouraged to hunt, so they lived for many weeks on roots, buds, and bark. When their enemies heard of that they called them Hadirondacks (tree eaters). That name was afterward given to the group of mountains where they had hidden.

SPIRITS OF THE HUDSON HIGHLANDS

Long, long ago the spirits who disobeyed Manitou were imprisoned in the Highlands. When Shatemuc rushed down and opened a way to the sea, many of them escaped. The others hid in the glens and valleys on both sides of the river. When they hear the sounds of a storm they think it is Manitou coming to capture them. Then they try to hide among the rocks, and they howl and scream with fear. People who hear their screams think it is the wind.

✳   ✳   ✳

*The white people changed the name of the Shatemuc
to Hudson, in honor of Henry Hudson, who discovered
it in 1609. At that time all American explorers hoped
to find a river on which they could sail across the
continent to the Pacific Ocean. Hudson at first thought
he had found it, when he saw that the water of the
Shatemuc rose and fell with the ocean tides.*

THE NAUGHTY FAIRY

Cro Nest, a height by the Shatemuc, was the meeting
place of the fairies. There they went at midnight to
feast and dance. There they held councils and made
fairy laws, sitting in a ring on toadstools. And there
the fairy king once pronounced sentence on a fairy who
had done wrong. He was told to wash his wings in the
mist which the sturgeon leaves when he strikes.

When a fairy does wrong his wings lose their
strength and beauty. It is a long, steep way from Cro

Nest to the bank of the Shatemuc, and the little fairy had to climb over the rough stones all the way. Then he had to pull loose from the sand a black shell with a pearl lining. Then he had to search until he found a tiny flower cup and a stiff blade of grass. He put these into the shell, then pushed it out into the water.

He got in, and paddled with the blade of grass. But he had a very hard voyage. The water goblins saw that his wings drooped, and that they had lost their color. Then they knew he was in disgrace. They tossed his little boat, and tried to pull it down.

At last he came to the place where the sturgeon strikes. He caught a drop of the mist in his flower cup and washed his wings in it. In a moment they became as beautiful as they had been before. He began to paddle toward the shore, and now the water goblins did not tease him. They pushed his shell boat and tried to help him.

When he came to the river bank he tried his wings. They were strong again. He flew up to Cro Nest, and all were happy once more.

HATCHET ISLAND

When the red men had to leave the Adirondacks their chief, Peiskaret, paid one more visit to the forest where he used to hunt and fish. He stood a long while looking out over the lake, then took his tomahawk and threw it as far out as he could. An island rose out of the water where it sank. It is called Hatchet Island.

THE LEGEND OF MANHATTAN

When the world was new the island of Manhattan was the home of a manitou. It was rich in fruit and flowers of all kinds. The bay was then a beautiful lake, with gold and silver fish swimming in it. Then Shatemuc, King of Streams, tore his way through the mountains. He came down to the sea. He swept every growing thing off the island. He broke off pieces of it. They lie in the bay to this day. Then the manitou fled to the land beyond the Great Lakes.

✳ ✳ ✳

In 1613 Adriaen Block came to this region to buy furs from the Indians. When he was ready to return to Holland, his ship caught fire and was destroyed with all the cargo. The crew put up a few log cabins on Manhattan. This was the beginning of New Amsterdam, afterward called New York.

MANITOU HILL

Once no rain fell on Long Island for a long, long time. All the springs dried up. The only place where the red men could get any water was at Lake Ronkonkoma. But many were afraid to go there, and many lived too far away. They gathered in one place to pray for rain. When they had prayed they heard the voice of the Great Spirit. He bade the chief shoot an arrow into the air and watch where it fell. The chief obeyed, and a spring gushed forth where the arrow struck the earth. Then they named the place Manitou Hill.

LEGEND OF LONG ISLAND

Long, long ago the red men dared not fish in Lake Ronkonkoma. The fish in it were human beings who had passed out of this life and were going to another. A powerful spirit dwelt in the lake to protect them.

There was also another spirit, that of a young girl. Her lover had been lost in that lake, and she rowed about at night, seeking him. The red men always knew when she was rowing there, for her boat shone with a green light.

LEGEND OF THE ONTEORA

Long, long ago there dwelt in the region of Shatemuc a huge dragon. He killed and ate human beings. At one time he wished to bathe in the sea. As he was crawling along toward Shatemuc he met Manitou, and Manitou turned him to stone. Then his bones became high mountains, with many deep ravines and steep cliffs. In time they were covered with forests, and were very beautiful. The two hollows where the eyes of the dragon had been were near the top. They filled with water and became lakes. The red men named the mountains Onteora (Mountains of the Sky).

The Dutch settlers found many wildcats in these mountains, so they changed the name to Katzberg. It has since been changed to Catskills.

THE GODDESS OF THE WEATHER

Long, long ago the Onteora were the treasure house of the weather for all the country around Shatemuc. The goddess of the weather dwelt in the highest peaks. She let out the day and the night. She never let them both out at the same time, because she was afraid they would quarrel. She hung the new moons in the sky, and cut up the old moons for stars. She often sat on the mountain tops spinning clouds. When she had finished them she threw them to the winds. They blew the clouds about. If anyone showed the goddess disrespect the clouds were black and full of storms. Then she poured down floods of rain, that streamed down the mountain sides and carried off everything in its way. She sent out lightning that burned the lodges of those who had made fun of her. But when people treated her nicely the clouds were soft and pretty. Then she sent down just as much rain as the earth needed, and it fell softly and prettily.

Sometimes the goddess played jokes on the hunters. A hunter would follow a bear or a deer a long time, and when he caught up with it it would change into something else. He could not tell what it looked like. Then he knew it was the goddess who had played with him.

Garden Rock was the place she loved best. It was covered with vines and flowers. All hunters knew that the goddess often sat there, and that she did not wish to be disturbed. They never followed the game to Garden Rock. But one time a hunter lost his way, and when he found out where he was he had come to Garden Rock. He did not see the goddess. He saw many gourds with water in them. They were in the crotches of the trees. The hunter was very thirsty. He thought he would take one of the gourds and hurry away. Surely there could not be any harm in that. He took the nearest one. Then he ran. But he thought someone was following him, and turned to see. Then he stumbled over the roots of a tree and fell. The gourd broke. The water began to run down the slope. He could not understand how the gourd could have held so much water. It grew into a stream. The stream kept growing larger. It washed away the hunter. It kept on until it reached another stream, and followed this down to the Shatemuc. It flows into the Shatemuc to this day.

★   ★   ★

The stream that washed away the hunter is Kaaterskill Creek. It rises in one of the lakes which were the eyes of the dragon. It leaps down the mountain sides in a number of falls and cascades, and finally joins the Catskill.

DUYVIL'S DANSKAMER

Long, long ago there dwelt in the Onteora a people who were skilled in working metals. When they worked at their forges the smoke spread over the country. Then the people in the lowlands said, "This is Indian Summer."

Sometimes those men wished to go hunting or fishing, or go on the warpath. But they would not go unless Manitou was willing to help them. They gathered on a height by Shatemuc when the moon was full. There they built a fire. Then they brewed a strange liquor. Then they painted themselves. After that they sang and danced until Manitou appeared to them. If he looked like a harmless animal they knew he would help them. If he looked like a ferocious beast they knew he was warning them.

As Henry Hudson traveled up the Shatemuc, those men were having one of their revels. When he and his men saw the antics of those queer creatures, how they jumped and yelled, tumbled about and made strange faces, they believed them to be some of the imps or goblins the Indians told about, and they named the place Duyvil's Danskamer. They were discovered by the dancers and invited to join them, and they dared not refuse. They were also offered some of the drink that was made for the occasion. They found this very good, and learned how it was made. Altogether, they enjoyed themselves so much that they agreed among themselves to come back to the Onteora, once every twenty years, and have a revel of their own.

THE

Lower
Mississippi
Valley
STATES

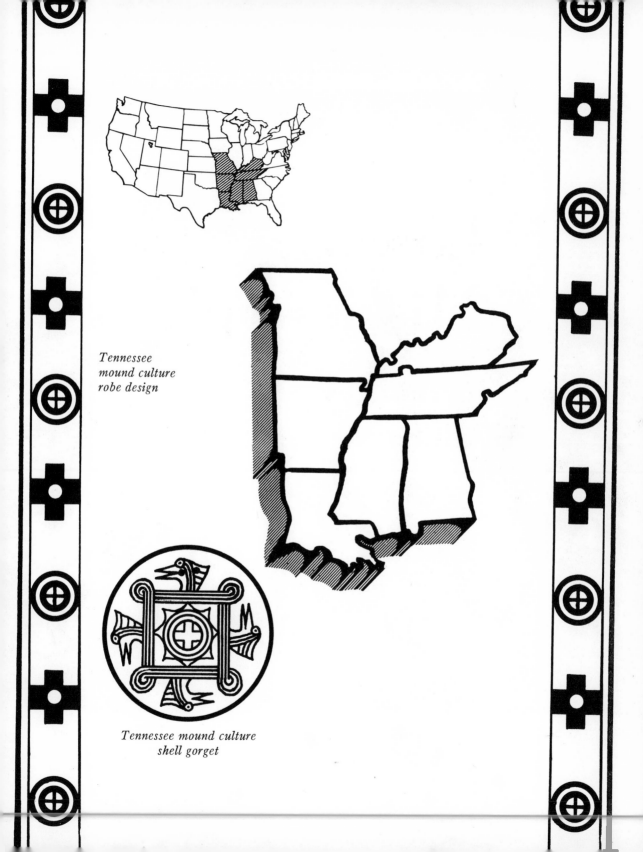

*Tennessee
mound culture
robe design*

*Tennessee mound culture
shell gorget*

"*Then he was no longer a
snail. He was a tall man.*"
—THE LEGEND OF THE
OSAGE TRIBE

Legend of Missouri

THE LEGEND OF THE OSAGE TRIBE

Long, long ago a snail once lay on the bank of the Osage River. The river began to rise. The snail clung to a log. The river rose higher and higher. It carried the log with it to the place where the Osage flows into Old Muddy Water (Missouri).

Then the river began to fall. The log was left on the muddy bank. The sun shone on the snail all day

long. He felt very warm. He could not move, and he thought he must die.

All at once his shell broke. He raised his head out of the mud. He felt that he was growing. His body grew large. Legs and arms grew out of it. Feet grew out of his legs, and hands grew out of his arms. Toes grew out of his feet, and fingers grew out of his hands. Then he was no longer a snail. He was a tall man.

At first he did not know anything. He was very hungry, but he did not know how to get food. Then the Great Spirit came to him. He gave the man a bow and arrows, and taught him to shoot deer. Then he showed the man how to take off the skin, to build a fire, and cook the meat of the deer, and how to make himself clothes out of the skin.

Then the man began to remember the place he came from, and thought he would go back. After a long time he found the place where he lay when the flood came. A beaver now had his house in the river bank. The beaver came out and told the man to go away, because the place belonged to him. The man said no, it belonged to him. He had lived there first. That made him owner of the land. They quarreled so that the beaver's daughter heard them. She came out and tried to make peace.

The man liked her. He said to the beaver, "The river is wide enough for us both. Give me your daughter, and you may keep half of it."

The man married the beaver's daughter. They became the first parents of the Osage tribe. No Osage Indian will hunt beaver, for they are his brothers.

"*He threw himself in the roaring stream, and was carried away.*"—ORIGIN OF SPRING RIVER

Legend of Arkansas

ORIGIN OF SPRING RIVER

Long, long ago the red men once gathered in the Ozark Mountains to celebrate a wedding. The bride was Nitilita, daughter of a chief. The bridegroom was a young man who owned hundreds of horses. The wedding was to last a whole month. But no rain fell for weeks, and the streams went dry. Some young men were sent to get water from Great River (Mississippi). No one felt uneasy because there was no water. The young men would soon return. In the meantime the dancing and the games went on.

But the young men stayed away very long. People began to suffer for want of water. Some became sick. Then some of them died. One of these was Nitilita, the bride. The bridegroom was beside himself with grief. He struck his head against a rock. He struck it so hard that he also died.

Soon afterward the young men came with the water. The chief gave orders that they be put to death. That was partly as a punishment, and partly as a sacrifice for those whose death they had caused. A large grave was opened, and the young men were buried together. Then a deep roar was heard from the earth. The ground trembled and opened. A stream burst through the opening and rushed down into the valley. Then the chief was overcome by grief, fear and repentance. He threw himself in the roaring stream, and was carried away.

In the twilight the red men often gathered on the banks of Spring River. It seemed to them that the faces of those who had perished there showed through the water.

Legend of Louisiana

CHIEF OPALEETA

Long, long ago there lived in this country a wise and good chief named Opaleeta. Once, when he was very old, he fell into Bayou Lacombe. He was under the water a long time. When he was found at last, his friends thought his spirit had left this world. But they did not give up. They tried and tried to bring him back to life, while the medicine men prayed and worked charms.

At last the old chief awoke. But he did not seem pleased. He told the other chiefs and the medicine men that he would far rather have been left to die, for the way to the happy Under Land lay through Bayou Lacombe, and he had been all the way to the gates. The air there is so mild and nourishing that no one needs any other food. The sun always shines

"Many . . . gazed into its clear waters, to see if they could see their friends . . ."—CHIEF OPALEETA

brightly, but it is never too warm. There is never any winter. The fields are dotted with red, blue, and golden flowers. The fragrance of them fills the air and makes it sweet. The grass is as fine as the hair of a doe. The streams are thick with honey. Beautiful birds fly about under the bright-colored skies. The stars dance to the music of the winds. There no one can rob the red man of what belongs to him. No one can teach him to do that which is wrong. At sunset those who have loved each other in this world get together. They sing songs of joy and gratitude. Their voices are always soft and sweet. Their faces are young once more, and beam with happiness. They will never be parted again, for there is no death in the happy Under Land.

The old chief Opaleeta told all this to the other chiefs and the medicine men, but they did not let anyone else know. For they were afraid that if everyone knew of the way to the happy Under Land the old, sick, and feeble would not wait, but would try to go there before it was time. But in some way the

people found out that the way went through Bayou
Lacombe. Many went there and gazed into its clear
waters, to see if they could see their friends that had
gone to the happy Under Land. They never saw

anything but the beautiful blue sky, reflected in the water. For those who are down there never go near the shores. They fear that their friends here may see them and call them back.

Legends of Mississippi

HOW THE EARTH WAS MADE

When the world was new all the earth was covered with water. Crawfish was sent down to bring up a little mud. He brought all he could hold in his claws. It grew bigger and bigger. At last there was all the land we see.

Then, at the place called Natchez, the Great Mystery made the red men. At first they did not know how to do anything. A spirit was sent down to teach them. He dwelt in the mounds which are still to be seen in that country. He showed the red men how to cook their food. He showed them what to do when they were wounded. The red men built a temple at Natchez. They called it the Temple of the Sun. When it was finished they laid a fire on the altar. A ball of fire came from heaven and lit it.

✗　✗　✗

The Natchez Indians were skilled in making pottery and baskets. They lived in nine villages. After being defeated in war with the white people they joined other tribes. In time they merged with these tribes and lost their own tribal identity.

The city of Natchez was founded in 1716, when the French built a trading post there.

LEGEND OF THE BILOXI

When the world was new a tribe of red men came up out of the sea. They were called Biloxi. Their goddess was a beautiful mermaid. They played wonderful music to her. When the white people began to come they wished to make all the red men worship their God. If any refused they treated them cruelly. So the Biloxi made believe that they worshipped Him, but they still prayed to their mermaid goddess in secret.

One night they were all awakened by the sound of wings. They also thought they heard the water in the river rise. They all went out. The moon was shining brightly. It shone on the river. All the water was heaped up in a great mound. On the top of the mound stood a mermaid.

When all the tribe had gathered around the quivering mound, the mermaid sang, "Come to me, children of the sea. Neither bell, nor book, nor cross shall win you from your queen."

The Biloxi were charmed by the beautiful mermaid and her song. They moved nearer and nearer. At last they were all standing close to the mound. Then the water fell back into its place with a hiss and a roar. All the Biloxi were buried under it. They were carried to caves beneath the river. There they dwell to this day. They still play their sweet music. The sound of it can be heard when the moon shines on the river.

FATHER DAMION'S DREAM

When the country was first settled, a good man named Father Damion came from over the sea to teach the red men, as well as his own people. In one of his

"... the Great Mystery ... showed the red men how to cook their food."—HOW THE EARTH WAS MADE

"When the storm had passed, the ring hung on the great bough."—THE CHIEF'S PROMISE

wanderings about the country he was lost. After walking about until he was tired, he came to the homes of some friendly red men. They gave him food and a place to rest. He fell asleep, and his mother came to him in a dream. She told him to follow the roses which grew in abundance in this part of the country. They would lead him back to his own people.

For days and days Father Damion followed the Cherokee roses. Sometimes they grew over swamps and streams, where he had to wade. Sometimes they were twisted together with other plants that wounded him and tore his clothes. At last, after many hardships, he came to Biloxi by the sea. When Sauvolle, the commander of the fort, had heard the story of the wanderer, he fell upon his knees and made a promise to build the first chapel at Biloxi.

THE CHIEF'S PROMISE

A warrior from the Natchez country loved a maiden of the Biloxi. Her father was a chief. When the warrior asked him for his daughter the chief pointed to a tree, from which one very large bough grew out, and said, "When the branches of that tree twist themselves into a ring, and that ring hangs on the great bough, and you can see the blue sky through it—then shall I allow my daughter to leave her home and her people and go away with a stranger."

Soon after this a whirlwind swept the whole coast. It broke many twigs from the great tree. But they did not fall to the ground or blow away. They circled round and round in the air, and finally twisted themselves together into a ring. When the storm had passed, the ring hung on the great bough. People looked through it and saw the blue sky.

THE
Great Lakes
STATES

*Ojibway bead
(sugar-maple)
design*

Ojibway calumet

Legends of Michigan

THE LEGEND OF MICHILLIMACKINAC

When the world was new Gitche Manitou once took a grain of sand from the bottom of the sea and let it float on top of the water. He cared for it and made it grow. At last it became all the land there is. Gitche Manitou chose for his own dwelling-place an island, which has been named Michillimackinac. There he planted beautiful gardens.

Then he made the red men. He made them that they might care for his gardens. Then he made animals. He made them for food for the red men. The red men showed their gratitude to Gitche Manitou by making sacrifices. After death they went to the Happy Hunting Grounds. These were beyond the Rocky Mountains. Some were ungrateful, and never made sacrifices. After death these were doomed to wander about the Great Lakes. They were watched by giants that never slept. These giants were ten times as big as men. They dwelt in the heights on Michillimackinac. Each was the abode of a spirit, and Manitou himself dwelt in the one named Sugar Loaf.

✳   ✳   ✳

Michillimackinac was the name of all the country around, and the capital was on the island. The fur traders had a station there, and a mission was established by the Jesuit fathers. Marquette spent the winter of 1669-1670 on the island, which we call Mackinac Island.

THE MAGIC MIRROR

Gitche Manitou had a son and a daughter. His daughter was to rule the sun, moon, and stars, and his son was to rule the earth. But the son wished to have all. He tried to kill his sister.

The sister had a mirror, made of polished stone, in which she could see what was going on around and behind her. She could also see what was in the hearts of people. Her brother did not know of this mirror. All his attempts to kill her failed.

When Gitche Manitou found out what his son was trying to do, he banished him. He sent him to dwell on one of the stars. Then he let daughter rule the earth also. Son dwelt on the star for ages and ages. Then he begged to be allowed to come back to earth. He would not harm his sister. Gitche Manitou let him come. But when he met his sister all his evil feelings returned. He drew his sword and tried to kill her. She held up her mirror. The sword struck the mirror and smashed it. It was smashed into atoms. They were scattered all over the world. Each atom afterward became a manitou.

THE FISHNET

Beside the manitou and the spirits, there were many deities among the animals. One of these was Great Hare, who dwelt on Michillimackinac. One day

"*...it was very easy for the little Puckwudjinnies to drop the burrs on him...*"—THE VERY STRONG MAN

"*Her favorite place was under the drooping branches of a tall pine.*"—THE PINE TREE'S BRIDE

"*She was so beautiful that he...kept her hidden in a covered boat...*"—THE LEGEND OF BELLE ISLE

Dick West

"*But the son wished to have all. He tried to kill his sister.*"—THE MAGIC MIRROR

"*He watched the spider...and made a large, strong net the same way.*"—THE FISHNET

Great Hare saw a spider making a web. He watched the spider, and saw how he did his work. Then Great Hare made a large, strong net the same way. He tried to catch fish in it, and was successful. Then he taught the red men to make fishnets.

THE STORMS ON LAKE MICHIGAN

Long, long ago a wicked manitou dwelt in the country about Little Traverse Bay. He was called Motche Manitou. One day the red men held a council, and decided to put a stop to his evil deeds. They took Motche Manitou and threw him into the bay. There he lies to this day. Once in a while he tries to get out. Then the water is disturbed, and furious storms rage over the lake.

THE PUNISHMENT OF LAKE MICHIGAN

At one time Nanabojo Manitou was very hungry. He ate so much that he got sleepy. Then he lay down

beside the lake and went to sleep. The waves dashed
over him, but he slept so soundly he did not feel it.
When he awoke he was all wet. Then he became
angry and said to the lake, "After this you shall
become smaller and smaller."

Ever since, the water has been sinking, and Lake
Michigan gets a few inches lower every year.

THE LEGEND OF BELLE ISLE

Long, long ago a manitou named Sleeping Bear
lived where Detroit is now. He had one daughter.
She was so beautiful that he was afraid to let anyone
see her. He kept her hidden in a covered boat in the
river. The boat was fastened to a tree with rope.
Once a day Sleeping Bear pulled the boat ashore.
Then he gave his daughter food, and let a woman
comb her long, glossy hair. He never let anyone else
see her.

But one time the Winds happened to see her as
she left the boat. They were charmed by her beauty.

Each one wished to carry off the boat and get the beautiful maiden. They fought about the boat. They pushed and pulled it about, each one a different way.

At last the rope broke. The boat danced away over the waves of the Huron. It came to the gates of the lake. These were guarded by old Ishkon Daimeke. When the boat went through the gates he had a glimpse of the maiden. He was charmed by her beauty. He kept the boat, and took the maiden to his own house.

When the Winds saw this they flew into a rage. They fell upon old Ishkon Daimeke and beat and buffeted him to death. They tore up his meadows and threw them into the lake. They lie there to this day. Then the Winds fell upon the boat, smashed it, and threw the pieces back into the river. There they became joined together and changed to an island.

Sleeping Bear took his daughter to the island, and placed a guard of poisonous serpents around it. The serpents are gone, but the island is here to this day. It is named Belle Isle.

⋆   ⋆   ⋆

*Belle Isle is in Detroit River, opposite the city.
Its area is about eight hundred acres. It belongs to
the city of Detroit, and has been made into a
beautiful park.*

THE IMAGE OF BELLE ISLE

Long, long ago the red men raised an image on
this island, and prayed to it. When the white men
came they wished to stop them from doing that. They
thought the best way to stop it would be to destroy
the image. Two of them went to the island and pulled
down the image. Then they broke it into pieces. They
threw the largest pieces into the river.

The red men had hurried to the island. They
were horrified at these actions. They stood about,
waiting to see the white men punished. Then they
heard a voice. It came from the pieces that had been
thrown into the river. It called aloud to the faithful
red men, asking them to throw the rest of the image

into the water. They obeyed the voice. Then all the pieces joined together, and became a large serpent.

After that no one dared to travel on the river. But a long time after, a great and good man, named La Salle, came to this place. He sailed up the river. Then weird shapes rose out of the water and followed his ship. They pushed it out of the river. They pushed it over the lakes. They pushed it so far that it never came back.

THE VERY STRONG MAN

Long, long ago there dwelt by the Pauwating a very strong man. His name was Kwasind. He did not know how strong he was.

One day his father sent him to wring out a net. Kwasind rolled the net together and when he began to wring it the net broke.

One day he and his father went hunting. The wind had blown down many great trees. They lay across the trail.

"We must take the other trail," said Kwasind's father, "but I shall smoke my pipe first."

When he had finished smoking Kwasind had lifted the trees out of the way.

The little Puckwudjinnies used to meet and dance in the Pauwating. They heard of Kwasind, and how strong he was. It made them jealous. They said, "When the red men hear of Kwasind and how strong he is, they will think he can help them more than we can. They will go to him instead of coming to us."

And they thought they had better get rid of Kwasind. They knew that the only thing that could hurt him was the burr of the white pine. They knew that the only place where he could be hurt was the top of his head.

The little Puckwudjinnies began to gather the burrs of the white pine. They gathered a great number, and took them to the red rocks that jut out into the Pauwating. Then they began to dance and play. All who passed by saw their white plumes skip on the water.

At last Kwasind came in his boat. But he did not see the white plumes of the little Puckwudjinnies. The day was very warm, and Kwasind had lain down in the bottom of his boat and gone to sleep. His head was bare. Now it was very easy for the little Puckwudjinnies to drop the burrs on him and kill the very strong man.

✳   ✳   ✳

The Pauwating is now called St. Mary's River.

THE SPIRITS OF PICTURED ROCKS

Long, long ago the Pictured Rocks were inhabited by many different spirits. The Storm Spirits, who ruled over Gitche Gumee (Lake Superior), dwelt at La Chapelle. When the red men wished to cross the lake they went first to La Chapelle. There they prayed, with many ceremonies, to the spirits, that they might allow them to make the journey in safety.

At Le Grande Portal dwelt a number of imps. They could never be seen, but the red men knew they

were there, for they played them many tricks. One of these was to repeat every word that was spoken by those who passed through the Portal.

The Pictured Rocks are so close to the water that they seem to rise out of Lake Superior. They have been worn into many wonderful shapes and colors by the waves.

THE WITCH

Long, long ago a hunter lived near Pictured Rocks. He had a wife and two children, and he was very kind to them.

One day a man who was related to him died. Then the hunter took the widow to his home, that he might care for her. He did not know that she was a witch. She saw that the hunter always gave his wife the best parts of their food. She saw that when he returned from hunting he always laid aside the best skins for his wife. Then she became jealous.

The hunter had made a grapevine swing by the shore. It hung over the lake. One day, when he was away, the witch offered to give his wife a swing. She made the swing go very fast. Then she cut the vines, and the swing fell into the water.

When the hunter came home he went to the shore to his children. The older child told him that their mother had been gone a long time. He was afraid she had been lost or killed. The hunter thrust his spear into the ground. He prayed that if his wife were dead, he might find her body. He wished to bury it decently.

Then a bolt of lightning struck the water. It made the lake rise and fall in huge waves. A roar of thunder shook the earth. Out of the waves rose a gull. It flew to the shore and alighted beside the children. The hunter saw a belt of embroidered leather around the bird. He knew the belt. It belonged to his wife. He caught the bird, and it changed back to its right shape. It was his wife.

When the witch saw them enter the wigwam she gave a scream. Then she disappeared. The next moment an ugly black bird flew out of the tent. It flew away between the trees. They never saw it again. They never saw the witch again.

THE PINE TREE'S BRIDE

Long, long ago the little Puckwudjinnies dwelt on the shore of Gitche Gumee. Their favorite place was a sacred grove of pine trees.

A little maiden among the red people was very

fond of hearing stories about them, and about the small manitou. She often went to the grove. Her favorite place was under the drooping branches of a tall pine. There she pretended that she was playing with the Puckwudjinnies, and she talked to the small manitou, and believed that they talked to her.

When she grew up her parents wanted her to marry a man whom she did not like. She knew she must obey them. She went to the sacred grove. There she leaned against the tall pine tree and wept.

All at once she heard a voice. It said, "O maiden, have you not always been more at home in the sacred grove and in the woods than you have in the village where your people live? Have you not always loved the small manitou and the little Puckwudjinnies? Are they not dearer to you than your own people? Why should you forsake them to wed a man you do not love? I love you, O maiden. I watched you play when you were a little child. I have seen you dream in the shadow of my branches. Stay here, and be my bride."

The maiden did not return to her people. She remained in the grove, and became the bride of the pine tree.

THE CITY IN THE SKY

Long, long ago there was a city near Lake Gogebic. The people who dwelt there were the best people in the world at that time. This made the people about them jealous. They troubled the good people in every way they could think of. Then the people of the city asked the Great Spirit to help them. He lifted the whole city up into the sky. While they were down here they played wonderful music, and now wonderful music is often heard from the sky above the lake. Sometimes at sunrise the city can be seen in the sky.

MANIBOZHO AND PAUPUKKEEWIS

At one time the snow was very deep and the red men suffered hunger. They could not hunt, for all tracks and traps were buried. They could not fish, for out on Gitche Gumee the ice lay piled up, so that it looked like great forts. Then Paupukkeewis said, "I shall go to the Kabibonokka and ask for help." Kabibonokka were the spirits who dwelt in the great ice forts.

Paupukkeewis took a big sack and went out to the ice forts. He told the Kabibonokka how hungry the red men were. They told him to fill his sack with snow and ice, take it to a hill they showed him, and leave it there. But he must not look behind him on the way. Next morning he must go to the hill and get his sack.

Paupukkeewis filled his sack with snow and ice. Then he dragged it to the hill. He heard voices calling insulting words after him, but he did not turn around to look. Next morning, when he came to get his sack, it was full of fine fish.

Now there was great joy in the camp. Manibozho was there, and he was invited to the feast. Paupukkeewis told how he got his fish. He was very careful to tell that he had not looked behind him while going to the hill.

Soon after, Manibozho took a big sack and went out to the Kabibonokka to ask for help. They told him to fill his sack with snow and ice, take it to a hill they showed him, and leave it there. But he must not look behind him on the way. Next morning he must go to the hill and get his sack.

Manibozho filled his sack with snow and ice. Then he dragged it to the hill. He heard voices calling after him, "Mukumik, Mukumik." That means "Thief, thief." He turned to see who it was that so insulted him. But he saw no one. It was only the wind in the bare branches, that sounded like voices. Next morning, when Manibozho came to get his sack, it was full of snow and ice.

Every winter, when the snow lies deep, Manibozho runs over the hills, dragging his big sack, and Paupukkeewis runs after him, calling, "Mukumik, Mukumik."

When the whirling snow sifts into the wigwam

and makes people draw closer to the fire, someone always remarks, "Paupukkeewis is gathering his harvest." And the red men smile.

Legends of Wisconsin

MANIBOZHO AND GREAT BEAVER

When the world was new Manibozho once made a dam in the Pauwating. Great Beaver broke down the dam. This caused the rapids which are in the Pauwating to this day.

When Great Beaver had broken down the dam he fled, but Manibozho pursued him. Great Beaver fled all the way across Gitche Gumee, and hid in Chequamegon Bay. There Manibozho could not get to him. Then Manibozho made a dam across the bay. He began at the south end, and left an opening at the north end. Then he went into the bay through the opening. But Great Beaver had gnawed through the dam at the south end, and escaped.

While Manibozho was building the dam he sometimes threw a handful of earth over his shoulder

into the lake. Each handful made an island. They are there to this day, and we call them Apostle Islands.

✳   ✳   ✳

The Apostle Islands are twenty-seven in number. French missionaries established a mission on the mainland in 1665, but later it was moved to Madeline Island.

The Pauwating, St. Mary's River, flows from Lake Superior into Lake Huron. The rapids are about one mile long. They are passed by means of canals, which have been built on both sides of the river.

THE RED SWAN

A young man once went hunting in unfamiliar country. He came to a pretty lake. There he saw a red swan swimming on the water. He shot an arrow at the swan. But at the same moment the swan rose and began to fly toward the West. It left a beautiful bright trail in the air.

The hunter followed the trail. At the end of the day he came to a wigwam. There he found an old man and a beautiful maiden. The man was making bows and arrows. The maiden was making moccasins. They received the hunter very kindly. He stayed overnight. In the morning he still saw the bright trail where the swan had flown toward the West. The young man now asked the old man for his daughter.

"Try to overtake the red swan," said the old man. "If you do that you are worthy of her. Then she shall be yours."

The hunter hastened to follow the bright trail. He followed it all day. At the end of the day he came to a wigwam. There he found an old man and a beautiful maiden. The maiden was more beautiful than the one he had asked to be his wife. The man was making bows and arrows. The maiden was making moccasins. They received the hunter very kindly. He stayed overnight. In the morning he still saw the bright trail where the swan had flown toward the West.

Nine days he followed the bright trail. Nine times he came to a wigwam, where an old man was making bows and arrows, and a beautiful maiden was making moccasins. Only each maiden was more beautiful than any of those he had seen before.

On the tenth day the sky glowed with the brightness of the trail. At the end of the day he came to a wigwam. There sat an old man, all alone. He was muttering strange formulas to himself. He was stirring roots and herbs, boiling in a kettle.

"Who gave you leave to come here and disturb me?" he asked.

The hunter told what had happened to him during the last ten days. Then he asked the old man if he

"He crawled, rolling and twisting, as serpents do."
—LEGEND OF WISCONSIN RIVER

"But Great Beaver gnawed through the dam . . . and escaped."—MANIBOZHO AND GREAT BEAVER

". . . the red men who lived by Gitche Gumee had a very large crop of corn."—THE CORN GOD

". . . he still saw the bright trail where the red swan had flown toward the West."
—THE RED SWAN

had seen the red swan. The old man did not answer, but he seemed uneasy. The wigwam glowed with a bright, warm light. The hunter stayed overnight. When morning came he prepared to follow the bright trail once more.

Then the old man said, "You have proved yourself worthy. Now you shall have your reward."

Then he opened the door and brought in a maiden. It was the maiden the hunter had asked to be his wife. Now he saw that the old man was her father. Now he saw that she was the red swan. Now she was more beautiful than before. She was the most beautiful maiden he had yet seen.

The old man said, "Take her to your own people and to your hunting grounds. The Great Spirit will protect you both."

LAC DU FLAMBEAU

Long, long ago a man and a woman dwelt on an island in this lake. They were the first people in the world. Their bodies were covered with shining scales. On the island was a garden with fine fruit. There were fields of corn and beans. The Great Spirit showed them one tree in the garden, and said, "You must not eat of the fruit of this tree."

One day, when they stood near that tree, they heard a voice. It said, "Why do you not eat of those beautiful fruits? They will make your hearts rejoice."

The man and woman looked at each other. They did not know what to do. They did not know who it was that had spoken to them. It might have been the Great Spirit. At last they took some of the fruit and ate it. They thought it would do no harm, if they took just a little. But as soon as they began to eat, the scales fell off their bodies. Only those on the fingers and toes remained. But these had lost their brightness.

Then the island was changed to a desert. The man and woman were driven away from it. But the Great Spirit was merciful. He took them to the shore in his canoe. Then he gave the man a bow and arrows.

He told him that he would find game, which he might shoot. They could prepare food out of the flesh, and the woman could make clothes and moccasins from the skins.

$$\times \quad \times \quad \times$$

Lac du Flambeau was so named because people used to fish there at night by torchlight.

THE CORN GOD

At one time the red men who lived by Gitche Gumee had a very large crop of corn. That made them vain and wasteful. They ate more than they needed. They let a great part of the corn rot in the fields. The children were given stalks of corn to play with. They threw them in the mud.

When all the corn had been gathered the whole tribe went hunting. But they found no game, so they returned home. They had been careless in storing the corn, and when they came back they found that rats had eaten most of it. Now they saw nothing but hunger before them. It was almost winter, and they had no food.

Among them was an old man who had warned them against waste, but they had not listened. He made a long journey. When he returned he called the tribe together and spoke thus:

"I wandered far into the woods. I came to a wigwam, made of bark. When I entered I saw a dwarf. He was very weak and thin. He lay stretched out on a bed of ragged, filthy skins. I asked him who he was and how he had become so poor and miserable.

"He said, 'I am the corn god. It is your people who have made me what I am. I gave them a large crop. They rewarded me with ingratitude. That is the cause of their suffering. It is also the cause of mine. I have no water in my jar. I have no clothes to keep the cold away. I have not even leaves to cover myself with. Weeds grow in my garden. Wild beasts prowl around my dwelling. Return to your people and tell them this.' "

When the old man had finished speaking the tribe knew what he meant. It was their own wastefulness that had caused their suffering. They still had a little corn left. This they now stored away very carefully, and lived on whatever they could find during the winter. When spring came they worked their fields with care. Then they planted the corn. This year they had also got a rich crop. They took good care of it, and never wasted anything again.

LEGEND OF WISCONSIN RIVER

Long, long ago a great serpent dwelt in the Mississippi. He wished to visit the Great Lakes, but he thought it would take too long to go all around by means of the waterways. Instead he went across land to Green Bay. He crawled, rolling and twisting, as serpents do. His body made long hollows in the ground. These filled with water, and became a river. In several places the serpent coiled up to rest. The hollows he made there also filled with water, and became lakes.

⋆   ⋆   ⋆

Father Marquette and Joliet were the first white men to travel on the Wisconsin River. Joliet had received orders to find the passage across the country to the South Sea (The Pacific), which was thought to be not very far away. From the Wisconsin they entered the Mississippi, and made many important discoveries.

DEATH'S DOOR

Two centuries ago Spirit Island (Washington Island) was the home of a tribe of Potawatomi. They were the greatest hunters west of the Mississippi. The long cape between the lake and the bay was their hunting ground.

At one time a band of Chippewa came to hunt on the cape. The Chippewa and the Potawatomi were friends. They had never yet met on the warpath. But to invade the hunting grounds of another tribe is a crime. No red man can forgive that. The Potawatomi prepared to punish the Chippewa. They started out across the water in more than one hundred canoes.

The water they had to cross belonged to Manitou. The red men never set out on it without making sacrifice. But this time they were in such a hurry they forgot to sacrifice. Neither did they remember to pray to Manitou for help. When they were half way across, Manitou sent a great wave from the south. It swept over every canoe, pulling them down into the deep.

For days the friends of the dead wandered by the shore. There the bodies were cast up by the waves, and each one took away his own and buried them. Since that time no red man will come within a day's journey of the cape or of Washington Island, as the island is now called. But the place where they were punished by Manitou is called Death's Door to this day.

✳   ✳   ✳

Death's Door is only six miles wide, but it is probably the most dangerous mail route in the country.

In summer, when the mail is taken across by boat, it is a pleasure trip. In winter, a covered sleigh is used when the ice is firm enough, and if the wind is right, sails are put up. But in autumn, when the ice is forming, in spring, when it is breaking up, and during a mild winter, "The Door" is filled with floating ice. Then the duty of the mail carriers calls for as great courage as was ever required of any soldier. They must take both "runners and oars," as they say. When they come to a large cake of floating ice they change their boat into a sleigh by putting runners under it. When they get into open water the runners are removed and the oars used. The mail includes any kind of baggage that is sent to or from Washington Island, as there is no other way of transporting it while navigation is closed. In addition to this, the mail men are often asked to take passengers, whose safety they must look out for.

In fine weather the trip across The Door is made in a few hours. In stormy weather it may take all day and night. There have been times when the men returned only in time to put on dry clothes and eat breakfast before setting out on the next trip. For they have pledged their word to Uncle Sam to start at the same hour every morning.

THE MANITOU IN DEVIL'S LAKE

Long, long ago a manitou dwelt in this lake. All the fish in the lake were protected by him. So was all the game in the country round about the lake. No red man would fish or hunt there. Neither would he take water from the lake, even though he was ready to perish from thirst.

The manitou was displeased if anyone tried to watch him. Once he shot an arrow at an offender, but missed his aim. The arrow struck a rock, which is called Cleft Rock to this day. An inquisitive chief, who was spying about the lake, was changed into a stone. It is called Cleopatra's Needle.

Devil's Doorway and Black Monument are seats which the manitou erected for his own use. There he sat when he wished to enjoy the beautiful scenery, and when he watched the spirits that sometimes ride about in the air, which some call the northern lights.

Legends of Illinois

THE PIASA

Long, long ago there dwelt in the region of the Mississippi a monster bird called the Piasa. That means man-eater. His face was like that of a man. He had horns like a deer. He had a beard like a tiger, and a tail like a fish. The tail was so long that it went twice around his body, then over his head and between his legs. The body was covered with scales.

The Piasa had a cave in the river bank. Pictures of the bird were drawn upon the rocks nearby. When the red men had to pass the pictures they were in great fear. They always rowed as close to the opposite bank as they could. No one dared look at the dreadful pictures, for they had power to harm. Many, while passing, tried to pacify the monster with loud wailings and lamentations. Others tried to pacify him with prayers and offerings. But the greatest number shot poisoned arrows against the cliffs, which were full of the marks they had made.

The Piasa often bathed in the river. Then the water rose above the banks, and the country was flooded. Whenever the Piasa saw a red man he flew into a rage. Then he struck his great tail against the ground, and the earth shook and trembled. He stole down so slyly that no one saw him until he was just above his victim. Then he carried him to his cave and ate him up.

Hundreds of brave warriors tried to kill the monster, and lost their own lives. At last the great chief Ouatoga decided to try. First he went off alone to fast and pray. This he did for one month. Then the Great Spirit told him what to do.

He took twenty of his braves and placed them near the rock where he saw the Piasa. It was a place where the bird could not see them. He told them to wait until the bird was just above him, then all shoot

"... the Great Spirit ... sent down thunderbolts ..."—THE LEGEND OF THE MASTODON

"Soon the monster came rushing toward him. Then Ouatoga sang his death song."—THE PIASA

"He looked like a swan, but was ten times as large."—THE LEGEND OF ROCK ISLAND

their arrows at it at the same time. Then Ouatoga took his own place where the bird could see him.

Soon the monster came rushing toward him. Then Ouatoga sang his death song. He knew that if the braves did not do just as they had been told, then he, too, must die. But they were ready, and they remembered what they had been told to do. When the bird was just above Ouatoga, all shot their arrows at the same moment. Every arrow struck the Piasa. He gave a scream that was heard far across the river. Then he fell down, dead. Ouatoga had saved his people.

The pictures of the Piasa were near Alton, and could still be discerned in 1860. The first white men who looked upon them were Father Marquette, the French missionary, and Joliet, the trader. Marquette described the monster and drew a copy of the pictures in his record of their journey down the Mississippi, which was made in 1673.

THE EVIL SPIRIT AT STARVED ROCK

Long, long ago an evil spirit dwelt near Starved Rock. He carried off little children. He dared not attack grown people, for he was afraid of their sharp-pointed arrows. All the children were terrified. They dared not leave their homes to play. They dared not go to the woods for fruit or flowers. They dared not go to the river to swim or catch fish. The Storm Spirit heard of this and it made him very angry. One night he struck the evil spirit so hard that he fell down into the canyon and died. He fell against a stone, and his great claws made marks in it. The red men showed these marks to their children. Then they knew they need not be afraid any more. Then they made a great feast, and everybody was happy.

Marquette and Joliet also traveled up the Illinois River, and founded a mission near Utica. Later La Salle and his trusty follower, Tonti "of the iron hand," built a fort on the high rock where the Jesuits had

built their church. About a century after the building of the fort, the Illini had become greatly reduced in number. They took refuge on the rock when attacked by a hostile tribe. The foe cut off their chance of escape, and prevented them from getting water, and "the last of the Illini" were extinguished by starvation. Since then the rock has been known as Starved Rock.

THE STORY OF LOLOMI

At one time Lolomi, daughter of Chief Blackhawk, stood on Starved Rock and watched a canoe going up the river. It was rowed by Uncas, the son of another chief. They were to be wed when he returned.

Uncas had painted a half moon on his canoe. He had told Lolomi that he would return when she saw the same sign in the sky. While he was away great preparations were made for the wedding. All the tribe loved Lolomi, and all rejoiced in her happiness.

Again Lolomi stood on the cliff and looked up the river. She had seen the half moon in the sky. But instead of her lover's canoe she saw another, rowed by a stranger. He was a messenger, sent by Uncas to tell Lolomi that he would not return. By this time he was married to another maiden. All the tribe grieved with Lolomi.

Once more Lolomi stood on the edge of the cliff. She threw herself from it into the river. All the tribe grieved for the death of Lolomi. She was buried after the manner of the red men, but first in the funeral procession walked a white man wearing a long, black robe.

THE LEGEND OF ROCK ISLAND

Long, long ago the red men called Rock Island their garden. It was covered with fruit-bearing trees and shrubs, and with edible plants and berries. A good spirit kept guard over the island. He looked like a swan, but was ten times as large. He dwelt in a cave in the river bank. The red men knew that the good spirit disliked noise, so they were always very quiet when they visited their garden. But when the palefaces came they built a fort on Rock Island. Then the good spirit fled far away.

THE LEGEND OF THE MASTODON

The Great Spirit created a number of animals for the benefit of the red men. He taught them how to prepare the flesh of some and use it for food. He taught them how to prepare the skins of some, and use them for clothing.

The Great Spirit also wished to give the red men one animal for a beast of burden, so he created the mastodon. This animal was powerful and invincible, and its hide was so hard that the sharpest spear could hardly pierce it. But the mastodon was fierce and ill-tempered, and instead of being of service to the red men, he became a menace. He also fought and killed the other animals.

At last all the animals in the forests and on the plains met and declared war against the mastodon.

The last battle was fought in the Ohio Valley, west of the Allegheny Mountains. The Great Spirit came down and watched it from a mountain top. The red men also watched it, for the Great Spirit had told them the mastodon would have to be destroyed, and they were ready to help if necessary.

It was a long and fearful battle. The ground was made soft and miry by the trampling of hoofs, and by all the blood that was mixed with it. (The marshes and mires are there to this day, and many bones of mastodons and other animals have been found in them.) The mastodons were fewer in number and, being so heavy, many of them sank into the mire and were drowned. But because of their immense strength, the ones that were left conquered.

When the Great Spirit saw that, he sent down thunderbolts from the mountain top to kill all the mastodons. One large bull caught the thunderbolts on his tusks and threw them aside. Then he fought until he was the only one left. When he found himself alone, he leaped the rivers, swam the Great Lakes,

and bounded into the far north, where he remains to this day.

So many useful animals had been killed in the battle, and so much of the ground made unfit for planting, that food became scarce for some time. Then the Great Spirit caused a berry to grow on the marshes, which the red men found good to eat. It was deep red, in memory of the great battle. It grows on the marshes to this day, and we call it the cranberry.

Pronouncing Vocabulary

(Indian speech has many sounds not duplicated in our own language. Therefore, the pronunciations given are intended only to translate these sounds into the nearest English equivalents.)

Adriaen ā′dri an

Agawam ag′ə wäm

Agiochooks ā′ ji ō chüks

Allegheny al′ ə gā′ni

Atotarhos ā′ tō tär′ōs

Bayou Lacombe bī′ü lä kômb′

Biloxi bi luk′si

Canandaigua kan′ ən dā′gwə

Cascade kas kād′

Champlain sham plān′

Chequamegon chə kwä′mē gon

Cherokee cher′ə kē

Chippewa chip′ ə wä

Damion dä mē ôhn′

Detsata det sä′tä

Duyvil's Danskamer dī′vilz däns′- kā mér

Gitche Gumee git′chē gü′mē

Gitche Manitou git′chē man′i tü

Glooskap glōs′kap

Gogebic gō gē′bik

Hadirondacks had′ ə ron′daks

Hinun hi nün′

Illini il li′ nī

Iroquois ir′ə kwoi

Ishkon Daimeke ish′kon dā mē′kē

Johan yü′hän

Joliet jō li et′ or zhō li ā′

Kaaterskill kô′térs kil

Kabibonokka ka′ bi bon′ ä kä

Kaskashaadi kas′ kə shä′di

Katahdin kä tä din′

Katzberg käts′bérg

Kineo kin′ē ō

Kwasind kwä sind′

Lac du Flambeau läk dū fläm bō′

La Chapelle lä shä pel′

Le Grande Portal lə gränd pôr täl′

Lelawala lē′ lä wô′lä

Lenawee len′ə wē

Lenni Lenape len′i len′ə pā

Lolomi lō lō′mi

Manibozho man′ i bä′zō

Marquette mär ket′

Mashapaug mash′ə pôg

Mauch Chunk mô chunk

Maushope mô shō′pē

Maywakan mā wä′kän

Merrimac mer'ə mak

Michillimackinac mich' i lə mak'-
ə nak (there are 70 listed spellings
of this name)

Minerwa mi nėr'wä

Mohegan mō hē'gən

Moqua mō'kwä

Motche Manitou mot'chē man'i tü

Mukumik mü kü mek'

Nanabojo nä' nä bō'jō

Nantucket nan tuk'ət

Narragansett nar' ə gan'sət

Natchez nach'əz

Nipmuck nip'muk

Nitilita ni' ti lē'tä

Nunnehi nun'nē hī

Oakana wä kä'nä

Oneida ō nī'dä

Oniagarah ō ni a'gə rə

Onoko ō nō'kō

Onondaga ō non' dä gä

Onota ō nō'tä

Onteora on' tē ô'rə

Opaleeta o' pə lē'tä

Osage ō'sāj

Ouatoga wä tō'gä

Passaconaway pas ə kon' ə wä

Paupukkeewis pô puk kē'wis

Pauwating pô wät ing'

Peiskaret pē' is kär'ət

Pemigewasset pe m̦i' jē wäs ət

Pennacook pen nä' kük

Penobscot pə nob'skot

Piasa pē' ə sô'

Potawatomi pot' ə wot'ə mi

Puckwidjinnies puk' wud jin'iz

Ronkonkoma ron' kon kō'mə

Saco sô'kō

Sachem sak'əm

Saratoga sar' ə tō'gə

Sauvolle sô vôl'

Sekonnet sek'ô net'

Seneca sen'ə kä

Shatemuc shat'ə muk

Sieur de Monts syėr də môn'

squaw skwô

Tonti ton'ti

Uncas un'käs

Utica ū'ti kä

Wando wän'dō

Wasawa wä' sə wä

Winnipesaukee win' nə pē sô'kē

Winona wi nō'nä

Woksis wôk sis'

Wyngaard win'gärd

Index

STAFF EDITOR: Milton Belkin

Type specifications:

Text: 14 Old Style No. 7
Major display: Bernhard Modern Bold
Internal heads: 12 No. 3 Gothic Copperplate Medium
Folios and running heads: 6 No. 1 Gothic Copperplate Bold and Light
Captions: 9 Old Style No. 7